fewer m

less worry

STATION 42

better decisions

GREG S. REID

STATION 42

Fewer mistakes, less worry, better decisions

Greg S. Reid

Joint Venture Publishing

Blue Sky R&D, LLC

Printed in the United States of America

TABLE OF CONTENTS

1

The Ticket

 Giving the house one last inspection, Sara walked through the two-bedroom cape cod where she grew up. Her bedroom, which until a month ago had remained exactly like it had been when she was a teenager, bore no resemblance to the girl she once was. Like the rest of the house, the wood floors had been refinished and the walls were freshly painted.

Getting her parents' house ready to sell had been quite a task. Her mom and dad hadn't made any cosmetic changes in the last 20 years, and it showed. Sara knew the honey-colored oak kitchen cabinets and laminate countertops were outdated, so updating the kitchen was a good investment that would attract buyers and increase her asking price. But like in so many projects, one thing always led to another. The bright new kitchen made the living room and dining room look old and dingy, so she tackled them. Of course, refinishing the floors in one room meant that she had to continue the process throughout the entire house. By the time she was done, the kitchen and bathroom were new from floor to ceiling, and the entire house had a fresh, new facelift — one that anyone could call home … except her.

Without her parents, it was a house, but it was not home. Sara was an only child, and when her mother died just nine months after her father's death, she inherited the house they bought shortly after she was born. Several decades later, the task of getting the house ready to put on the market had been time consuming and difficult. Everywhere she turned, she found another memory — her grandmother's rosary hung on her mother's dresser mirror, her father's military tags were tucked away in his top drawer, and framed photos of Sara during various stages of her childhood were displayed throughout the house.

But it was the doorframe that flooded her with emotions. Every year on her birthday, her father stood her against the doorframe in her bedroom and etched a small mark into the wood to mark her height and permanently document her growth. Seeing the notches, Sara knew that the doorframe had to be replaced, but she wasn't prepared for the onslaught of tears when she removed the board — the last item in the house that still contained any memory or reflection that the three of them had ever lived there.

With a sigh, she walked her way through the house, verifying that it was ready for new owners, a new family to come in and make it their own. At the front door, she flipped the switch, turning off the new chandelier she had bought for the entryway, chosen specifically to catch the eye of prospective buyers, with the hope that it would make a statement and impress them the moment they walked in.

After closing the front door, she turned to verify that it was locked, and that's when she noticed the old mailbox. Next to the freshly painted front door, it hung crooked and looked tired in the space that she'd tried to make welcoming. With a sigh, she knew it would have to be replaced, so she pulled a screwdriver from her small bag of tools and set out to remove it. While unscrewing it from the brick wall, one side of the mailbox fell down, exposing an envelope that must have somehow slipped and gotten stuck between the mailbox and the porch wall at some point in time. Turning it over, Sara was surprised to see that the envelope was addressed to her, and even more surprised to see that it was date stamped nearly a quarter of a century earlier, when she was only 13 years old.

Sitting on the front porch, she carefully opened the envelope and unfolded the letter that was tucked inside. Immediately recognizing her grandfather's distinct handwriting, she read the 23-year-old letter for the first time.

> *Sweetheart,*
>
> *Your grandma and I would love for you to visit us. Here is an open-ended first-class train ticket to take care of your fare. Let us know when we can expect you. We are so looking forward to seeing you this summer!*
>
> *All our love,*
>
> *Grandpa and Grandma*

How she wished she had known! Shaking her head in disbelief, she wished she had received the letter those many years ago. If she had, she would have jumped on the next train, excited to be able to visit the grandparents she dearly loved. But she hadn't known about the letter, the ticket, or the fact that they had made a special effort to spend time with her.

It was another loss—she'd lost her grandparents and her parents and now came to terms with the fact that she had lost an opportunity. All that was left was a letter and the ticket she held between her fingers. She gazed down at the ticket, which simply said:

FULL FARE	
ROUND TRIP ECONOMY DEPARTURE: STATION 42 # 0 1 7 3 2	

Welcome to Station 42

 It was two weeks later when Sara decided to use her train ticket. Her ex-husband had their eleven-year-old daughter, Abby, for the week. Recently divorced, sharing custody was new to both of them. While the marriage had not been salvageable, Sara and her ex both had their daughter's best interests at heart, and they agreed that Abby needed both of her parents in her life. It had been quite an adjustment for Sara, whose life had revolved around their daughter for the last 11 years, but she had slowly come to appreciate some time alone. It was a luxury she hadn't had for a long time.

As she dressed for the train ride, her mind went back to the days when boarding and riding the train was a special event. Men wore their best suits and ties, often stopping outside the station to have their shoes shined, and women dressed in their finest dresses, hats, pearls, and patent leather pumps, after spending their day in curlers to make sure their hair was perfect for such an occasion. At least, that's how she recalled her parents preparing before they departed from Station 42 for the next town, where they would dine out on the weekend from time to time.

Times had changed, however. Sara walked into Station 42 wearing a pair of black pants, flat loafers, and a stylish jacket. To others, she looked like she might be going to work or, perhaps, simply meeting a friend in another town for lunch. But she was doing neither; Sara had no agenda for the day other than to take a ride on the train.

When she entered, the once bustling Station 42 appeared to be abandoned. Four ticket windows were unmanned and obviously had been for some time. An older gentleman at the only open window tore his eyes from a paperback book just long enough to see who had walked through the station's double doors.

"Hi," she said to the man. "Can you take a look at this ticket and tell me if it's still good? My grandfather sent it to me years ago."

After examining the ticket, he passed it back to her.

"Haven't seen one like that in quite some time, but yes, it's still good," he remarked.

"Great! Can you tell me when the next train leaves for Roberts?" she inquired.

"Every two hours, on the hour," he said. "The next train will leave at 10 AM."

With some time to wait, Sara took a seat on one of the marble benches in the train depot and gazed at her surroundings. The once magnificent stone and marble architecture was showing its age. About 100 years old, the marble was dull and cracked in several places, and the glass chandeliers that graced its ceiling had lost their glisten and sparkle, as well. But yet, as if they were stamped in time, the original ornate molding and arched windows were still there, although any light filtered through the windows was filtered by years of dust and dirt, both inside and out.

At one time, Station 42 was a pillar of the community, the hub of progress and social activity. But today, it was empty, a landmark from a bygone era that had been replaced by two-car families and Ubers. Apparently, passenger trains were a thing of the past, unless one lived in a big city, like New York, where mass transit still thrived, and the Subway was still one of the main modes of transportation.

It was ten minutes later that she heard a faint train whistle, signaling that the train was approaching Station 42 to pick up its passengers. Sara walked outside and patiently waited to show her 20-plus year-old ticket to the ticket taker before boarding.

She didn't quite know what to expect, but she felt slightly let down when she realized that she was the only passenger in the entire train car. As her eyes passed over the rows of empty seats, she quickly settled on a window seat, thinking that was what she would have chosen if she had used the ticket when she was a young girl.

Settled in the seat, she looked out the window at the familiar town where she'd grown up and lived all her life. It was a small middle-class town, perfect for raising families, that sat about 30 miles west of Jefferson, a city that had enjoyed the growth which had evaded her hometown over the last couple decades.

Sara looked up when the whistle blew, signaling their departure from Station 42. At that exact moment, another woman boarded the train and quickly caught her eye.

"Is anyone sitting here?" she smiled, motioning to the seat next to Sara.

"No, it seems like it's just us," Sara replied.

"It's nice to have a little company on the morning train," the older woman said. "I usually travel solo."

"It looks like trains are a thing of the past," the younger woman remarked with a hint of sadness in her statement.

"Perhaps, but I love taking the train. It's convenient, affordable, and a part of my past. Oh, listen to me go on. I haven't even introduced myself. I'm Elizabeth Roberts. Most people call me Liz."

"Nice to meet you, Liz. I'm Sara Andrews."

"So, Sara, what brings you aboard the train at Station 42 today?" Liz inquired.

"It's a long story," Sara answered, before sharing her discovery of the long-lost ticket with the stranger next to her.

"How fascinating! That's a story you can tell your grandchildren someday. So tell me, do you have children?"

Sara spoke with pride as she spent the next several minutes telling the elegantly-dressed woman about Abby. Then she turned the conversation toward her traveling companion.

"How about you? How many children do you have?" she asked.

"Me? I don't have any children. In my younger years, I was too busy working in the family businesses to have time to raise a family," Liz answered. "I guess you could say my work has been my family."

"Oh? What do you do?" asked the younger passenger.

"Right now, I'm in real estate development, but over the years, I guess you could say I've dabbled in a little bit of everything," said Liz.

"Such as?" Sara asked, genuinely curious.

"I started working in my grandfather's seed store when I was 10, and let's see, I've worked at my father's hardware store, then the five and dime. When I graduated from high school, I became a teller at the only bank in town, and then…"

"What town?" Sara interrupted.

"Well, Roberts, of course," Liz smiled.

"Wait … Roberts? *The* Roberts? Don't tell me that you are one of the Roberts that owns the whole town? The Roberts State Bank? Roberts Tools and Hardware? Roberts Five and Dime? Oh my, I used to go to all those places when I was a kid!" Sara exclaimed.

"Well, we *used* to own all of those places. Most of them have been sold by now, and some have been replaced by big box stores. But, yes, the town was named after my family," Liz explained.

"That's incredible. I can't believe that I'm sitting here talking to a member of the family who founded the town where I'm going to spend the day. What a coincidence!"

"Do you have business in town?" asked Liz.

"No, I don't, but I thought this trip would provide me with a good opportunity to look for a job. Now that I'm divorced, I need to return to the workforce and become financially independent. It's time for me to create some security for me and Abby," she said.

"What type of work are you looking for?" the older woman asked.

"I'm not sure. I don't have a college degree, so I guess I was just going to get an idea of what's available. I've been a full-time mother and homemaker since Abby was born, so I definitely need some professional experience," Sara said, tucking her dark brown hair behind her ear, something she did when she was worried or became anxious.

"Well, perhaps I can help you," Liz interjected.

"How?" Sara replied, unsure what her fellow passenger was referring to.

"Here's my business card," the woman said. "Meet me at this address after lunch if you can, and we'll talk some more."

Sara gazed at the business card, which read, "Roberts Development Group, Elizabeth Roberts, Founder. A Roberts Family Venture." Before she could say a word, the train's brakes were engaged, and their trip came to a stop at the Roberts Train Station.

"Here we are," the older woman announced. "I'll see you at 1:00."

Departing the train, Sara immediately noticed the difference in atmosphere in the two train stations. While Station 42 was a shell of its former self, there was a line of passengers waiting to board in Roberts, a sign of the city's prosperity and growth. Young and old alike, it was obvious that travel by train was alive and well in this flourishing town.

Perhaps, she thought, *some of that growth will rub off on me ... and perhaps Liz will be part of that.*

A few minutes before one o'clock, she walked through the doors of Roberts Development Group, a large office building designed with function in mind, while still representing the historic aspects of the town it was named after.

While Sara paused to admire her surroundings, she looked around to find someone who could help her. Noticing that the reception desk was unmanned, she turned to take a seat in one of the strategically placed seating arrangements nearby.

"Oh, there you are!" Liz exclaimed, quickly walking toward her. "I hope you haven't waited long."

"Not at all," Sara replied, jumping to her feet. "As a matter of fact, I just got here."

"Good. Come, let's go to my office and talk," the company's founder said, leading her to an office just around the corner.

The two women sat at a table in Liz's office, where Liz asked a lot of questions of the young woman. What type of work was she looking for? What were her goals? What were her strengths? Where did she see herself in five years? Ten years?

"I guess I'm a little rusty," Sara explained. "I haven't had a job since Abby was born. Since then, I've been busy taking care of our house and family, so I don't really have experience and haven't given much thought to my future … until recently, that is."

"Well, I'd say spending a decade organizing a house and family is experience," remarked the older woman. "More than that, I enjoyed our talk this morning. You are personable, pleasant, and approachable. Those are all admirable qualities in business. I guess what I'm trying to say is, if you're willing, I'd like to offer you a job. You might have noticed that our reception desk is empty, and I know Shannon could use some help."

"Who is Shannon?"

"She's my right hand. Unofficially, I call her my secret weapon," Liz smiled. "Behind the scenes, she keeps this show running."

"It sounds amazing, but I don't know if I'm qualified," Sara hesitated.

"Don't worry. We'll teach you what you need to know. It's an interesting industry, Sara, and I think you could learn a lot," informed the owner.

After talking for another 30 minutes, Sara agreed to start her new position the next Monday. Shaking the hand of her new employer and friend, she thanked her for the opportunity and told her she hoped she wouldn't let her down.

"I believe we all have something to offer, Sara. And life has shown me time and again that people come into our lives when we need them. Perhaps there is a reason why you were led to the train and Station 42 when you were," Liz proposed. "While it was a trip your grandparents wanted you to take, I hope it is a trip that you can look back on and be grateful you took."

$$\textcircled{3}$$

Ask Gus

Featuring Shannon Parsons

 The next Monday morning, Sara was greeted by a slender woman with long dark hair.

"Hi, you must be Sara. I'm Shannon Parsons, Liz's executive assistant," she introduced herself.

"It's good to meet you, Shannon. Liz, uh, Ms. Roberts, spoke highly of you," Sara replied, correcting herself.

"Around here, we all call her Liz," Shannon smiled. "She'll be a few minutes but said for me to show you around until she's done."

As Shannon gave her a tour of the facilities, Sara asked how long she had been with the company.

"I've been here for about five years now," she said.

"Did you know that you wanted to be in this industry when you started?" asked Sara.

"I knew I wanted to do something more than what I was doing. I guess you could say I knew there was more out there for me, but I didn't know what it was at the time," Shannon said.

"So how did you end up here at Roberts?"

"I asked GUS," Shannon smiled broadly.

"Who's GUS?" Sara asked, confused.

"GUS stands for God, Universe, and Spirit. Instead of praying to God or just using the Law of Attraction, I talk to GUS. It came about because praying to God didn't feel like it was the right fit for me. I knew the energy I felt when I prayed was expansive, but I didn't know what to call it. That's when the idea of GUS came to me," Shannon said.

"I like it!" Sara exclaimed.

"So do I. It reminds me of the little happy-go-lucky mouse from Cinderella. Gus the mouse makes me laugh. When there's something in my life that I'm wanting or needing, if I think of GUS and that mouse, it puts me in a childlike spirit. It makes me laugh, and it invokes a lightheartedness in me," she explained.

"Oh, my daughter loves Cinderella. I'm going to have to tell her about talking to GUS when she wants something," Sara laughed.

"It works for children and adults. As I've told this story to others, GUS has developed quite the following, and I've been told by many people that they're talking to GUS, too," said Shannon.

"So GUS led you to this job? How did it come about?" Sara inquired.

"GUS is about combining affirmative prayer and the Law of Attraction. It involves seeing the positive side of things. You see, if we have any resistance about our needs or manifesting our desires, we aren't going to attract what we want in life. The lightheartedness is where all the magic is! It's the idea of letting ourselves off the hook for all the doubts we might have about whether or not we deserve things and releasing the fear around knowing *how* to actually get what we want. If there's something we want in life, we have to allow ourselves to expand and play with the idea as if we were a child, as if we *could* have everything we've ever wanted. A child going to Disneyland wants everything; they're in awe of everything."

"Isn't that the truth!" Sara agreed.

"GUS the mouse is in love with life. When you're in love with life and searching for the good, you'll find the good. I tell people to look for the good, the joys, and the blessings. It goes beyond gratitude and into the feeling of appreciation. When you're appreciating things, people, or feelings, you're in the moment. GUS is all about feeling at one with the incredible unconditional love and joy for everything around you. That creates a vibration, which attracts even more things like that," Shannon explained.

"So you asked GUS for a job, and GUS delivered?" Sara guessed.

"The day I met Liz, I was driving to a networking event, and I had been wanting to make a career change. But I didn't know what. I wanted something bigger and different, but I didn't know exactly what it was at that time. So I talked to GUS and told him, 'Alright, GUS, you know who I am. You know what I'm capable of. I don't know what I want, so I don't know what to ask for. So you need to put the right person and the right opportunity in my path and make it so obvious that they're sitting right next to me.' Two hours later, I was sitting right next to Liz, and we started a banter back and forth. As she talked, I found myself realizing that her ideas matched mine and I wanted to be part of her mission. Before I knew it, I was asking if she needed an assistant. And here I am. And it's all because of GUS!" Shannon smiled.

"That's just incredible. And I have to say, it's so similar to how I met Liz. She was literally the only person on the train when we met," Sara informed her new friend.

"Liz has a knack for finding great people. All it takes is for the other person to show up as themselves, being themselves in every way. That's my agreement with GUS, to show up as myself; someone who wants to connect with people and help them succeed. On the rare occasions when that doesn't get me what I want, I've learned to be patient, knowing that something better is out there for me," said Shannon.

"How amazing! Hopefully, GUS will help me find the answers I'm looking for," Sara said.

"He will. GUS is awesome. Take it from me, if you ever want or need anything, or even if you need guidance about where to turn for answers, just ask GUS," the assistant suggested.

"Great! Will GUS teach me how to work this phone system?" Sara laughed.

"Even better, I will. We'll save GUS for bigger magic!" Shannon laughed.

Invest in Great Relationships

Featuring Bill Walsh

 That afternoon, Liz had an appointment with a speaker who was slated to give the company's keynote at their annual employee appreciation party. Liz valued her employees and strongly supported their personal and professional development and growth. Over lunch, she mentioned that she'd like Sara to join the meeting and take notes in order to follow up and make sure no details would be overlooked for the event.

Bill Walsh had flown in that morning from Chicago, where his office was based. Sara discovered that he was a prolific speaker and bestselling author who focused on success and marketing principles for entrepreneurs. As Sara glanced over his bio, she was in awe that she was sitting in the audience of someone with such an impressive background.

In the conference room, Liz discussed the topics he would speak about at the event and shared with him the key points she wanted her employees to take away. Sara focused on making sure she took detailed notes and documenting the items that Liz indicated she would need to create the featured speaker's profile and bio.

About an hour into the meeting, Shannon tapped on the door, indicating that one of Liz's general contractors needed to speak with her urgently.

"I do have to take this call," Liz stated. "Sara, can you keep Mr. Walsh company for a few minutes?"

It was Bill who started the conversation.

"So how long have you worked for Roberts Development?" he asked.

"To be honest, today is my first day," the new employee admitted. "I have no idea what I'm doing yet."

"That's exciting. So I take it you're interested in real estate development?" he asked.

"Well, yes. At least I can say I'm interested in learning more about it. I'm just thankful that Liz gave me this opportunity. I have to admit that I'm excited about listening to your keynote. I think I can learn a lot from you as I embark on a career," she stated. "Until then, I'd appreciate any advice you can give me."

"Here is what I tell every aspiring entrepreneur, but it applies to any career. If you want to go fast, go by yourself. If you want to go far, then go with a great team."

"I'm not sure that applies to me. You see, I don't have any experience at all. I've spent the last 12 years being a mother and homemaker," Sara shared.

"No matter where you are in life, you have something called

experience," Bill stated. "Obviously, you do have experience. You have the toughest and greatest job in the world, which is being a mom. If you can do that, you can do anything. Start with that premise. Then based on whatever you're great at, that serves a lot of people, and there's money in the space and you're passionate about it, that's where you start a business."

"I'm entry level, so I'm not there just yet," Sara replied.

"There's nothing wrong with having a job, two jobs, or three jobs. That will give you what I call peace-of-mind money. You need that money to pay your bills. Having more than one job is often part of the rally of an entrepreneur, especially if they don't have much capital. But while you're doing that, you have to begin to invest in great relationships. So you have to immediately put yourself in the places where people who have had the most success in your industry are. For example, if you want to connect with millionaires, go to vistage.com events. At the most basic level, there are rotaries and Chambers of Commerce where you can meet people. I also often advise people to have a book cover designed, even if they don't have a book yet. A book cover displayed on a website will open doors and create interest, which can help you get in the right places with the right people."

"And that will really help me to succeed down the road?" she asked.

"Sara, there's an old saying that if you hang out with four broke people, you'll be the fifth. But if you hang out with the most successful people in your industry, some of it will rub off on you. One of the first things I teach is to get rid of the people who don't believe in you. The idea of investing in great relationships is to get yourself around great people who are already wildly successful in doing what you want to do and who are connected to your future perfect customer," Bill advised. "You have a good start in working here with Liz."

"I agree," Sara said. "And I'm grateful that I can learn from her."

"In the sense of gratitude, it's important that you don't just turn to them to give you what you want. You want to go there with the intention of adding value, whether that means you're checking people in, setting up chairs, or making phone calls. Do whatever it takes to help those who play at that high level. Do what you say you're going to do. The truth is the most successful people pay attention to those who add value first and expect nothing in return."

"I've never thought of it that way," she admitted.

"If you can learn that process, you'll start to realize how beneficial it is. But you have to become persistently consistent. By doing that, you'll discover the fastest way to hyper growth and momentum is through relationships. Invest in them, add value, and it's proven over time that you'll be successful," Bill informed her.

The door opened, and they turned their heads to welcome Liz back in the meeting.

"Please forgive the interruption," she said. "I trust that you two have had a nice talk?"

It was Sara who spoke first.

"Oh, yes! Bill has been extremely helpful and informative, and I thoroughly enjoyed our conversation. Now, how can I help the two of you make this the best event ever? I want to add value in any way I can," Sara said, flashing a smile toward Bill, who simply nodded in approval at her initiative and desire to put his words of advice to use right away.

Be the Change You Wish to See

Featuring Emily Mishler of The Cultivated Group®

 It was two days before their annual employee appreciation dinner, and Roberts Development was abuzz with activity. Sara had dropped her daughter off with her ex-husband the night before; she wanted to get to work early the next morning, knowing that there was much to be done.

Arriving at the office, she immediately spotted Liz.

"Good morning," Sara said. "I thought I might see you on the train today."

"I drove today. I have to pick up a friend at the airport this afternoon. As a matter of fact, I was going to ask if you would do that for me. I have a meeting with the planning commission and surveyors this morning, and I have to be at the architect's office right after lunch. You can take my car. Here's the keys," Liz said. "Do you mind?"

"Wow, it sounds like you do have a full plate!" Sara agreed. "Of course, I'll be happy to pick up your friend at the airport. Where should I drop her off?"

"If you don't mind, just take her to her hotel, and I'll catch up with her later today. Tell her I'll swing by about 6:00 and take her out for a bite to eat," Liz stated, turning on her heels, already in pursuit of the next thing she needed to address in an all-too-busy day.

Sara climbed into Liz's Mercedes, taking a moment to experience the plushness of the seats, the rich smell of fine leather, and the smoothest humming of an engine she'd ever heard. After a few minutes on the road, she allowed herself to relax. She'd made the trip back and forth to the airport many times, but never in a high-end luxury car, which she reminded herself belonged to her employer. Still, she smiled, realizing that this was a first, one of many she'd had in the last several weeks, and she hoped the trend would continue.

Sara waited for her passenger, holding a sign that boldly stated "Ms. Emily Mishler." A woman walking toward her with luggage in-hand bore a friendly, warm, radiant smile with a genuine sparkle in her eyes; and Sara knew right away that she was Liz's friend.

After introducing herself, the two women climbed in the car and Sara asked Emily to tell her about herself.

"I'm an intrepid optimist with a keen sense of adventure, eye for design, hand in fundraising, and heart for philanthropy. I love to experience the fullness of life through travel, food, exploration, and savoring all of life's sweetness. In my "work life" (I don't believe there's much separation), I run a group of businesses called The Cultivated Group®, which is a growing portfolio of five companies: Cultivated Ventures, Cultivated Change, Cultivated Press, Cultivated Creative, and The Elevated Method®," Emily explained.

"What do you do?" Sara asked.

"We work with clients (individuals and businesses) to empower, equip, and inspire them to 'be the change they wish to see in the world'—beginning in *their* world. Back in 2019, we created The Cultivated Group® with a vision for a future where impactful ideas, access to opportunity, and taking action to change and preserve the beautiful world in which we live is equitably accessible. Using our Fluid Framework® method, we use an industry-agnostic approach to connect the 'servant's heart' to the 'business brain' of impact-driven businesses. Everything we do is for the purpose of leaving the world better than we found it; more conscious, more connected, more kind, more joyful, more healed. Our mantra is to *be the change you want to see in the world* and inspire others to do the same," Emily replied.

"I like that!" Sara said.

"Thank you! I love it and am so grateful to be a part of it. So tell me about yourself," Emily said, reversing the roles.

"Well, I'm a single mother and a divorcee. My daughter, Abby, has been my whole life, until I started working for Liz a couple months ago," Sara informed. "It's been quite an education for a former stay-at-home mom and homemaker."

"It sounds like you've just jumped into the next chapter of your life!" Emily responded warmly, with a deep air of recognition and delight.

"Yes, I did—and with both feet! Do you have any advice for me?"

"I am thrilled for you, Sara. Having the courage to *truly engage in living your life* is something not many people do. It also sounds like you've begun the journey of creating your own definition of what success is and looks like, for you. And that, my friend, is where the unapologetic pursuit of your life lives. I've found that no matter what you do, personal responsibility is key. If you're able to hold yourself accountable to pursuing and nurturing the purpose of your life and surrounding yourself with people whose dreams and actions encourage yours, that becomes a breeding ground for transformation and evolution," Emily advised. "I admire that you've had the courage to be able to look at and assess your life, make a new decision and step into your power. There's so much courage there, and so much strength. That courage, strength, inspiration, and the passion that goes with them often makes the difference between those who *truly live* and those who are not fully engaged and living their life," Emily said.

"Sara, when I was finishing up an MBA, I was working full-time and had an internal nudge that told me there *had* to be something more. That nudge got louder and to a point I could no longer ignore it. I made an active decision to employ courage, take what felt like a very large risk, and pivot away from the 'direct path' to a career I was very well positioned for. I left everything I knew and bought a one-way ticket to Hong Kong and started travelling the world full time. That nudge, or guidance, is something I now actively use daily. Our stories are very different in the way we've experienced life, but the common thread of intuitive guidance is there," Emily shared.

"Wow. That does take courage!" explained Sara.

"Yes, and every step has been absolutely worth it. After traveling by myself for 18 months, I created these companies that serve different clients and help empower businesses to make a difference in the world through the systems we build and consulting we do that ultimately empower their bottom line. Out of that experience has come an incredibly fulfilling project of my own that became a children's book series called Esmè the Curious Cat®. This children's book series is the medium through which I communicate the life lessons, inspiration, beauty, connection, and the common threads of humanity that I experience while travelling for our world's future: our children. All I've done is follow the breadcrumbs, healed myself, surrendered control to the Universe, and taken aligned action in the directions I am led. From my experience, when you're experiencing a potential pivot and feel turbulence, simply beginning can feel terrifying. Just know that stepping forward into what you know to be true is one of the most important keys to that," Emily smiled.

"Your background is just incredible, Emily, and I can only hope to be as confident in my decisions one day as you are!"

"Just remember that you have the ability to exercise the power of choice. Sometimes we are quick to overlook the seemingly simple ability we have to choose our response over a reaction in any situation we are presented with. That is often our greatest power. Choosing our response determines the character that we employ and who we become," Emily told her.

"I'm so glad that I got the opportunity to meet you and talk with you, Emily, especially given the fact that I've been wondering if I am making the right choices. Don't get me wrong—I like Liz and my job. I'm learning so much that it can be overwhelming, but I also sometimes wonder if I'm spending too much time away from my daughter, or if I'm being selfish. You've helped me to see that my choices can benefit me, as well as others, especially my daughter," Sara admitted.

"Being a living example of the change you wish to see in the world will not only transform your life, it will also have a strong impact on your daughter. It might be the best example you can ever be to her, Sara. Living my truth and these lessons has been a cornerstone of my success and the success of the businesses we work with around the world. That's why Liz invited me to her annual award ceremony—she's a woman who has embraced change and used it to enhance the lives of the people around her. Every year, she includes philanthropy and contribution in her annual goals, and I'll be presenting those to her employees and partners at the event. It's part of the change I want to see, part of the change Liz wants to see, and I think you'll find that it's the change you want to see, as well," Emily smiled.

"I'm excited to listen to your presentation. Oh, look, your hotel is up ahead on the right. Liz asked me to drop you off and let you get settled, but she did say she'd pick you up around six o'clock and join you for dinner," Sara said, remembering her employer's instructions.

"Will you be joining us?" asked Emily.

"Oh, no. My daughter has soccer practice tonight, and I need to be there. But I'll be at the event and will see you there," Sara replied.

"Good. It was great meeting you. I'll be wishing you my best as you continue to grow, and thanks so much for the ride, Sara," Emily said.

"You're welcome. Thank *you* for being an inspiration to me and so many others who don't have the courage to listen to that nudge, take action, and make a difference. Your story and encouragement have inspired me to make changes in my own life, so I can have an impact on others," Sara said. "You know, I think Liz can sense my hesitation to move forward in my life. Do you think that's why she asked me to pick you up?"

Emily laughed, "Liz always seems to find a way to make a difference in the lives of those she cares about."

Discover Your Greatness

Featuring Kelly Cardenas

 The employee appreciation dinner was a celebration, indeed. Liz had gone overboard to make sure her employees at Roberts Development knew they were truly appreciated. Not overlooking a single detail, she had hired a professional planner to transform the large conference room into a spectacular showpiece.

Every chair was covered with the finest linens drawn together with beautiful satin bows, and each table was adorned with a centerpiece that replicated some of their greatest developments. Along the wall was a large table full of appetizers to please any palate, from charcuterie boards to oysters. At the front of the room, a large cake that was an identical replica of Roberts Development took up an entire table, together with a cupcake for every employee, frosted with the talented hand of a baker who beautifully scripted the tops of each with an employee's name.

The servers were professionally dressed in crisp white tuxedo shirts closed at the collar with black bow ties. While they were formal, they were friendly, making sure they spoke to every guest with a smile and a kind word. After they'd cleared the plates from the delicious four-course dinner, they disappeared behind the scenes when Liz took the floor.

First, she introduced her friend, Bill Walsh, who gave an impressive speech on how to turn inspiration into success that captured the audience's attention from start to finish. When he was done, Liz returned to the front of the room to introduce the next speaker.

"I hope everyone had a great meal and is enjoying their evening," she said. "Before we move on to the entertainment portion of our evening, we have the pleasure of having a guest speaker who has not only impacted me and my career, but I am proud to say is my dear friend. Without further ado, I'd like to introduce you to Kelly Cardenas. I met Kelly as my hairdresser years ago. Since that time, I've realized what an amazing connection he has been in my life, and I hope you invite him into yours, as well. Please give a warm welcome to my close friend, Kelly Cardenas."

Taking the stage, Kelly waited momentarily for the applause to wind down before beginning.

"As Liz said," he opened, "we are close friends who met because she sat in my chair. That story is the basis of my career and my success. Yes, my background is in the professional beauty industry. I've owned salons throughout the country, and I've traveled and educated people throughout the world for 29 years, speaking to individuals, companies, and organizations.

"I'd like to tell you a little about myself and how I became the owner of a multi-million-dollar business and a worldwide speaker. None of my success would have been possible if it wasn't for the fact that I have two phenomenal parents, two kids who love me, and a wife who has taught me how to love. I am really blessed," Kelly continued.

"My background and experience helped me realize that people were the foundation of my success, and hair was the conduit to get to people. When I started on my journey, I knew it wasn't all about cutting hair; it was about being able to touch lives. Let me explain.

"Today, I am privileged to speak to people, companies, and organizations, but I started with an audience of one that sat in my chair. Through that audience of one, I built systems where anyone could succeed. If they followed the systems, they could literally skyrocket their careers. I wanted to make it so simple that they wouldn't be focused on the actual task at hand. Instead, they would be focused on the person that they were working with and, most important, the connection they were making.

"That's what I built my empire on. It was systems based and always has been. But I want you to know that the emphasis hasn't been the systems. I always wanted to take the technical part out and simplify it as much as possible so we could focus on what really mattered, which is the people.

"The whole business was built on three principles: Number one, be really kind; number two, make friends; and number three, stay curious. Those three principles are based on a single principle that my father instilled in me at an early age, which is that success is 98 percent attitude and 2 percent aptitude. Because of that, I knew I never had to be the smartest one in the room; I just had to have really cool friends and a great attitude," he laughed. "And I know that is true for anyone, if they follow the systems I've put in place.

"My whole emphasis in talking to you this evening is to take you from an accomplishment mindset into an acceptance mindset. Remember, you are awesome. That's the first thing I want you to remember. Number two, you're beautiful just as you are. Don't compare yourself to anybody. Think about it: when you are yourself, you have no competition! And the third principle is that you can do anything that you put your mind to. However, remember that just because you put your mind to it, that doesn't make it your purpose. I found that as long as I was in line with my purpose and accepted my greatness, I didn't have to worry about accomplishing anything. I was able to sit in and accept that greatness. So can you," Kelly nodded to the audience.

"You might have noticed me walking around and mingling with all of you before dinner was served. When I speak to a company or an organization, I ask for access to the people in the organization. I do that because most people don't understand how awesome or beautiful they are. Once they grasp that, we can move forward and move into the three principles, which again are being kind, making friends, and staying curious. It's important that I have the opportunity to share that with my audience because I believe that you have to be kind to yourself before you can be kind to others in a meaningful way.

"Liz Roberts asked me to speak to you tonight and share the principles of my success, because we both adamantly believe those principles apply to every person, no matter what industry or career they are in. It all starts with being kind, and I mean more than smiling and being courteous. The kindness I refer to is at a deeper level, one that creates a connection by making a contribution. I encourage every one of you to make a contribution to every single person possible. When you're always contributing, everyone else gets what they need, and you'll never have to worry about yourself.

"How about making friends? How does that influence success? Making friends helps you with perspective. I like to think of it this way: one is too small of a number to succeed. Looking across the room at the team Liz has created, I think you can all agree with that," Kelly said.

"The third principle in my system is to stay curious. The more you want to know, the more you'll know. Children prove this principle to us every day. They ask questions over and over until they are satisfied with the answers they're given. They take things apart to see what's hidden inside and see the wonder and invisible possibilities in themselves and the world around them. Curiosity keeps their lives from being stagnant and boring, and it opens the imagination up to a world of exploration and discovery. I guarantee that curiosity is one of the greatest teachers you will ever know!

"The system is intended to be easy, and rightfully so! I knew it wasn't difficult because it was my dad who taught it to me. My dad always told me that I was the greatest. Because of those three principles, I started to be kind, I made friends, and I asked questions and let curiosity and wonder guide me, and my father told me I was the greatest every single day. That changed when my mom passed away, when he told me that I was the greatest and *to act accordingly*. He told me that if I act according to my greatness, everything else would fall in line. He was right. When

I acted according to my greatness, I took my success to a new level.

"I credit my parents with my success. The principles and beliefs that they raised me with were the foundation of my success. I've found so many people give you the method or the path to success, but when you have the foundation of understanding how awesome and beautiful you are, and that you can do anything you put your mind to, like my parents told me every day of my life, it will give you the wings to create magic in your life!

"You might wonder if my system really works, and I'm here to tell you that it does. I wasn't the smartest kid in school. As a matter of fact, I struggled and barely passed fourth grade. I could barely read or write, but still my parents kept telling me I was awesome. Because I was able to understand that and accept my own greatness, I didn't feel the need to compare myself to anybody else. I didn't feel inferior or doubt myself in any way. I was able to just be who I was. That enabled me to walk amongst giants and create a phenomenal life and a fantastic career. And it wasn't due to my aptitude; it was all because of my attitude. I got to where I am because I wanted to contribute to every person around me. I built a multi-million-dollar national company, and it wasn't because of what I know—it's because I knew these three principles.

"You can do it, too. You don't have to be in the beauty industry to implement my systems. The hair was just a conduit. I knew the basis of my career was larger than hair—it was the connection with people, much like Liz has with all of you. My mentor once told me that there is not a piece of hair that is not connected to a head, that's not connected to a body, that's not connected to a soul… and if you can touch the soul, you can do anything.

"As I stand before you, I can attest to the fact that there is only one business in the world, and that is the people business. If you take the people out of the business, there is no business at all. I know that. Liz Roberts knows that. And tonight, my purpose is to make sure you know that. You are awesome. You are beautiful, and you can do anything you put your mind to. You really matter—be kind to yourself. When you are, success will come naturally, easily, and sooner than you thought possible," Kelly finished. "Walk in your greatness, and greatness will follow."

Liz walked up and hugged her friend, thanking him for sharing the principles that he had taught her many years before. Taking the microphone, she added, "Not only does Kelly make people look beautiful, but he makes them realize that they *are* beautiful just as they are. It's one of the reasons I love and admire him so much. He's taught me to see the beauty in each of you, and that's a gift that I can only repay by helping you to see it in yourselves. I hope you enjoy your evening and celebrate your greatness. Thank you."

It Takes Courage, a Tribe, and a Coach

Featuring Mary-Frances Buckland

 It wasn't long before Sara realized that working full-time created challenges at home. Abby had always been used to having her mom home, or at least available whenever she needed her. On top of the divorce, it was yet one more change that her daughter resented. Lately, she placed that resentment entirely on her mother.

It was in her first month at Roberts Development that Abby became unreasonable, arguing about who was going to pick her up that day, and breaking Sara's heart when she said she never saw her anymore and wished things were the way they used to be.

It just so happened to be the same day that Liz took the train, too. When she boarded and sat next to Sara, she could tell the younger woman was preoccupied.

"Is something wrong?" Liz asked with genuine concern.

Sighing, Sara hesitated before answering.

"Yes. No. Well, I don't know. It's just my daughter. She's having a difficult time adjusting to the changes in our life, and she knows how to make me feel guilty," Sara replied.

"Oh, mommy guilt, huh? I've never had kids, so I can't say I know what you're going through. But I can say that you need to be easy on yourself. Change happens. Your daughter will adjust, Sara. I'm certain of that," Liz said.

"I wish I knew that for sure," Sara replied. "I guess I'm just struggling as much as she is at the moment. It's all so new, so different, and I think it will take time."

"I'm sure it will. If you don't mind some advice, though, it might be helpful for you to talk to people who do know what you're going through, people who have similar experiences," Liz suggested.

"Maybe, I considered joining a parenting group, but I don't need another thing on my plate just yet," Sara said.

"You might not need a parenting group, but I do think you need a tribe, a group of trusted friends who will give you support, encouragement, and guidance when you need it."

"That sounds perfect, but where do I go to find this tribe?" Sara asked.

"I would recommend that you meet some new people. And I know just the person. Her name is Mary-Frances Buckland. Actually, she's my life coach. But I know that she would be coming from a place where she understands what you're going through. For starters, she has children, and she's also divorced. Is it okay if I reach out to her and set something up?" Liz asked.

"You'd do that for me? That would be great. It would be awesome to be able to talk to someone who knows what I'm going through," Sara replied.

The next day, Sara met Mary-Frances for lunch.

"Hi, Sara," Mary-Frances said. "It's good to meet you."

"Thank you for agreeing to meet with me," Sara said.

"I'm happy to. Liz told me a bit about what you're going through. Hopefully, I can help," Mary-Frances said.

"I'd love that. Being divorced is new to me, and I don't think it's been easy on me or my daughter, Abby," Sara said. "Liz tells me you're a life coach?"

"Yes, I've been a coach and am currently in the process of starting my own coaching business. So, I guess I have both personal and professional experience in this area," she explained. "To start, I want you to know that I know this is foreign territory, for both you and your daughter. That said, I also want you to know that it's okay to be alone. If you're wondering if you can do this alone, I want you to know that you can. You don't have to have somebody there. The hole or the emptiness that needs to be filled doesn't necessarily need to be filled by a specific person."

"I think that's something I've been debating in my own head. It's good to know that someone understands that feeling."

"I do, and I want you to know that being alone can actually be beneficial. As a coach, I can tell you that sometimes when you're alone, you're least distracted and that's when you can find yourself, heal yourself, and grow the most," Mary-Frances advised. "Perhaps this will provide you with a positive opportunity to grow and improve. Let me remind you that it will benefit both you *and* your daughter. You have an opportunity to substantially improve both of your lives."

"I already have, so to speak. Liz offered me a position at Roberts Development, and I'm learning so much that my head is spinning sometimes. While there is a lot to learn and take in, it's been quite rewarding. I'm hopeful that this job leads to a real career," Sara said.

"I think you're already seeing that your life change is offering you new, exciting opportunities. That's a positive, Sara. It's evidence that you're not in your darkest hour. Sure, there may be times when you know you've had better days, but in the midst of it all, there is always something positive. For example, in retrospect, you can probably admit that you were in an unhealthy relationship, at least emotionally, and you are now removed from it. Use this time to create a healthy relationship with yourself. This is the time when you are free to grow and learn from your own experiences. Your past, of course, didn't happen *to* you; it happened *for* you. So don't carry any regrets," Mary-Frances encouraged.

"I don't regret the divorce, although I have to confess that I do regret how it is affecting Abby."

"Sara, your past built your foundation. Don't think about shoulda, woulda, coulda's ... you can't undo the past. I had to teach myself that as I navigated through my marriage and divorce. Instead, I encourage you look to today and the future. Pay attention to your dreams and use them as your focal point," Mary-Frances said.

"Is that what you did?"

"Yes, but to do that, I had to shift from thinking I had to go through it on my own. Sara, while you don't need to fill the hole in your life with a significant other, you do need people in your life. Use this time to find support within your tribe. Learn to accept help. Lean on others when you can. You'd be surprised how much it helps to know that you have a friend or a circle to turn to," Mary-Frances shared.

"Yes, Liz also suggested that I need friends," Sara replied.

"She's right. Build your own tribe who will support you and allow you to make the choices that are best for *you*. That tribe will also be there to help you talk things out. It's like having a soundboard to test the waters on before you dive on in," Mary-Frances said.

"You don't know how much I need that, especially on those days when Abby gives me grief, complaining that I'm not there all the time like I used to be. It's like she knows how to play the guilt card," said Sara.

"Kids are great at that, aren't they?" Mary-Frances smiled. "Don't worry, Sara, your daughter will forgive you. I know that. My kids support me *now*, but it took time for them to accept that our family dynamic had changed. Don't blame yourself for that. People change; relationships change. That's not your fault. You did what you could with the knowledge you had at the time."

Mary-Frances hit a nerve with those words, and Sara's eyes welled with tears. Inwardly, Sara did blame herself for the divorce. Sure, she and her husband hadn't been happy together in the end, but she often wondered if she should have stayed in the marriage, for her daughter's sake, if nothing else.

Seeing the emotion in Sara's face, Mary-Frances reassured her that it was normal, even beneficial.

"Honor your emotions as they flow. That's very big! If you feel like crying, go ahead and cry. Each time emotions arise, it helps you deal with them easier. If you bottle something up, Sara, it's like shaking a can of soda. Then when you open it, the lid just explodes!"

"Thank you. I guess I do need permission to struggle from time to time. Sometimes I tend to feel that because I wanted the divorce, it means that I shouldn't feel bad about it or how it's affected me, Abby, or my ex," Sara admitted. "Like yesterday morning, I felt so guilty and defeated that I was ready to throw my hands in the air and give up."

"Don't give up, but don't forget that there are people who are able and willing to help you. You've got a good mentor in Liz, and that is truly important. Everyone needs help along the way. Find your compass. Look for guidance and seek counsel," Mary-Frances encouraged.

"This is a good time to remind you that with every sunrise we are offered a new day of new opportunities. Look for the bright light! Like the moon, have the courage to shine when everything else is dark. That is so powerful! Whatever you do, Sara, don't go to the itty, bitty pity committee. Don't look at yourself as the victim. Think of yourself as the victor! You survived the marriage, and you've already survived the divorce—you just don't know it yet," Mary-Frances smiled.

"I know it's time to move on. I guess I just don't trust myself completely yet," Sara replied.

"That's something to think about. When you're moving on, don't over consume on education or things to divert your attention, because when you do that, you might end up giving your attention to nothing. It's like being so busy chasing glitter in the wind; with everything you have to do and take on, you have to learn to say no, not now. But you have to learn to say no to the *right* things—things that don't have a powerful impact and outreach," Mary-Frances stated. "I knew that there were things I *didn't* need in my life, but I also knew that one thing I *did* need was a friend."

"That's precisely what I need!" declared Sara.

"Well, you've got me, and I know what you're going through, Sara. I hope I can help you get through it stronger, healthier, and happier," said Mary-Frances.

8

Fail Fast

Featuring Eric Power

 Sara arrived at Station 42 early the next morning. After having dropped her daughter off at school, she went straight to the train station, figuring she'd do some research and, hopefully, find nearby events that she could attend, like Bill Walsh suggested. In the back of her mind, she also hoped to meet new people—*who knows*, she thought, *they might just become a member of my tribe one day.*

Expecting to walk into an empty building, like most days, she was surprised to find that she wasn't the only person in the train station. A table had been set up in the middle of the room, and a group of men were seated in the chairs around it. The first thing she noticed was that, while all of the men wore civilian clothes, they appeared to be servicemembers or perhaps veterans. One had a US Army ballcap on his head, and another simply wore fatigues. Another wore a t-shirt that had a picture of the US flag on it and a well-known military slogan.

Several minutes later, the meeting came to an end, with one gentleman inviting the others to contact him if they needed any help. After they shook hands and departed, Sara found herself catching his eye.

"Good morning," she said.

"It is a good morning," he replied.

"I can see that you got an early start to the day. I don't mean to intrude, but it looks like you were meeting with veterans. I only say that because my grandfather was one. I still have his medals," she remarked.

"Yes, we had an early meeting. And to answer your question, yes, we are all veterans, including me. I own a company that assists veterans in getting the benefits they deserve," he informed her.

"Really? First, let me thank you for your service. Oh, and my name is Sara Andrews," she said, reaching out and offering her hand.

"It's good to meet you, Sara. I'm Eric Power," he smiled.

"It's great to meet you. You obviously have a noble company, but I always thought disabled veterans automatically qualify for benefits. Are you saying they don't?" she asked.

"That's right. Unfortunately, there are thousands who are entitled who get turned down or receive less than they should," he nodded.

"And you have an inside track into the process?" she asked.

"Well, let's just say that I am a disabled veteran who realized that the process of applying and being approved for disability is far too complicated and difficult. I was turned down, but I refused to give up. Through the process, I figured out the right way to complete the paperwork. Since then, I have devoted my career to helping other veterans through my company, Veteran Disability Help," he said.

"You've made a career out of helping others? That must be rewarding," she replied.

"It is. We've helped thousands of vets and counting. And we won't stop until every disabled veteran gets what they are entitled to receive," he vowed.

Thinking back to her conversation with Bill Walsh, Sara had an idea.

"I'm not a veteran," she said. "However, I do want to help others and contribute to the community. If there is ever an occasion when you could use a volunteer to help, even if it's just to answer the phones, I'd welcome the opportunity. Hopefully, I could add value to your organization, and along the way, I could get a glimpse into your business. I'm just getting a start in the business world and feel like I have a lot of catching up to do. I want to learn as much as I can, from as many people as I can. Since you have created a successful business, can I ask your secret?"

"Secret?" Eric repeated, confused.

"Yes, your secret to success..."

"Oh. Insofar as volunteering, we are busy and could always use an extra hand, I assure you," Eric said. "And I'd say the secret to my success is letting myself fail."

"What?" Sara gasped. "Did I hear you right?"

"You sure did," Eric stated. "It was my mentor who taught me that failure is necessary for success. I learned early on that new entrepreneurs get discouraged so very easily. That would have been me if it wasn't for the fact that I had a mentor by my side. You see, I made mistakes and, yes, they drug me down. But my mentor showed me why I needed to view failure from a different perspective. He said it was great that I failed because failure was teaching me what not to do. He said it was the best thing that could happen. Imagine that!

"He said I needed to get through the failure and that it was a good thing it happened early in my career. I call it failing fast. Most people shy away from failure—they want to avoid it at all costs. But I now see that failure, and failing fast, as soon as possible, is one of the very best things that can happen. I got my mistakes out of the way right away. I learned what not to do, and then I was able to correct my course," Eric shared.

"I'll have to remember that, for sure," Sara said.

"It's an unusual concept, but I know how true it is. Everybody thinks knowing how to do the right thing is the secret to success. However, that's only half of the equation. It's just as much about learning what not to do so you don't repeat it. When you can get that lesson out of the way straight out of the gate, you won't repeat your mistakes and the path to success is wide open from there on out."

"I love it, Eric. So because you got your mistakes out of the way early, you don't make mistakes now?" she inquired.

"No! As an entrepreneur, I've learned that mistakes happen. They're inevitable. Sometimes I occasionally get a black eye, but now when I do, it's not as painful as it could have been. Thanks to my mentor, I know how to handle it," said Eric.

In the distance, a whistle signified that the next train was approaching the station.

"That's my call," Sara said, rising from her chair. "It's time to go to work. But I was sincere in my offer. Do have a business card so I can connect with you and volunteer to help your cause?"

"Absolutely," Eric said, handing her the information. "I look forward to hearing from you. Until then, find a mentor, someone who is experienced in what you want to do. They know how to succeed and how to fail and can teach you how to make the best of both of them."

Follow the Leader

Featuring Tina Malsom

 As the months went by, Liz and Sara spent a lot of time together. Shannon was taking on new responsibilities within the company, so Liz took Sara under her wing, teaching her everything she needed to know about real estate development. She showed her how to apply for permits and who to call for surveys. They talked about utilities and building codes, architects and blueprints, inspections, and drainage.

At times, Sara still felt overwhelmed with how much she was learning, but Liz was very patient and made sure she carefully explained everything, including who to turn to for answers or assistance.

"You do know a lot of people," Sara pointed out.

"I do. In this business, it's a necessity. I learned long ago that the more people you know, the better!" shared Liz. "It's never too early to build your network, Sara. That reminds me, there's a networking event coming up next week, and I think it would be a good idea if you went with me—that is, if you're free and have someone to watch Abby," said Liz.

Abby just so happened to have volleyball practice the evening of the event, so Sara arranged for her ex-husband to pick their daughter up and stay with her until she got home. It was at times like this that she was grateful that she and her ex-husband had maintained a cordial relationship and worked together to take care of their daughter.

She arrived at the event and immediately set out to find Liz, who was already deep in conversation with a group of people. Judging by their laughter, Sara was right in assuming they knew each other well.

"Sara! Glad to see that you made it," Liz said. "There's a really good turnout tonight. Why don't you grab yourself something to drink, and I'll be with you in just a bit?"

As she waited for a glass of wine, Sara was joined by a woman at the drink station.

"Hi, I'm Tina Malsom," the woman introduced herself.

"Hello, Tina! I'm Sara Andrews. You walked up at the right time. It's always awkward to me to stand at a bar by myself," Sara smiled.

"Well, you're not alone anymore," Tina said.

"Thank you! So, Tina, what do you do?"

"For the past 15 years, I've been a professional network marketer," she answered.

"Oh? How did you get into that?" Sara asked.

"You could say it was by accident. I was raised by traditional parents who expected me to go to school, get a career, and stay with it for the rest of my life. The plan was to work for 40 years, retire at 40 percent of my income, and then rely on another job when I ran out of money. I tried to do that. I went to school and picked a career. Then I switched careers. Eventually, I got a job at a medical supply company, mostly because I could bring my six-month-old son with me," Tina shared. "Over time, the owner of the company told me I could try my hand at sales and make commissions. When he said that, a light bulb went off for me."

"Do you like sales?"

"Oh, yes, and I was good at it. I became sales manager, then the VP of sales, then I went into marketing, then sales *and* marketing. From there, I became VP of sales and marketing, and 12 years later, I was the vice president of the whole company," Tina said.

"That sounds like an incredible career," Sara said, impressed.

"It was ... until I walked in one Monday morning and the company was gone," Tina shared.

"Gone?"

"Yes, without a word, the entire company moved across the state. I was instantly out of a job. As a single mom, I depended on certainty, so this was a very scary circumstance I never had expected," said Tina.

"What did you do?"

"I learned a great lesson—not to count on anyone to take care of myself and my son, except myself. I had to figure something out fast, and just as I was praying to the universe for a miracle to appear, I met a woman who was crushing it at network marketing. At first, I didn't believe that people could be really successful and make a lot of money doing that, but I found out that there were people making five times more than I had been and working less time to get it. So I signed up. And it has worked. There's a part of me that loves a goal and a challenge and the opportunity to make as much as I want based on my efforts," Tina explained. "The bonus was I could do it from home!"

"I take it you were successful?" Sara questioned.

"Yes. I know it's not for everybody, but I found that I really started to succeed when I was the one in control. So I invested in learning and educating myself through books like *Think and Grow Rich,* which was very influential to me. I found I was great at making friends and socializing," Tina said.

"You are! You are certainly making me feel comfortable," Sara shared.

"Well, thank you. Self-development has really helped me thrive. I've empowered myself along the way. I love working and earning income on my own terms and in my own lifestyle. I realized that it's the perfect career for me, especially when I looked at my old report cards, where teachers mentioned that I talked too much and was only motivated by rewards. Even as a child, I was motivated by a reward system, and network marketing provides that. We get paid to socialize! The more we talk and make friends, the better we do."

"You have a great point," Sara laughed.

"I know, right? I figured out how to use this 'gift' toward sales. Step one was to get people to know me and like me. To do that, I knew I had to make friends. That's how I worked my way to the top of several different companies. Sara, another teacher said that I have an innate ability to involve other people in my schemes, which is really funny now," Tina laughed. "But I can see now that is what team building is—it's about getting other people involved and excited about your vision and then working toward it with you."

"I bet you're good at that!" Sara pointed out.

"I've had to learn a lot along the way. You might find it hard to believe, but the first time I spoke on stage, I hated it. Then I heard that the people standing on stage make the most money. I think the saying is, the person with the clicker gets paid quicker. So I had to learn how to get over my stage fright and speak in front of an audience. Then I had to figure out what to speak about," Tina admitted.

"What topic did you decide on?"

"I came up with a signature speech that's worked well for me. It's called 'Everything I learned about network marketing, I learned in kindergarten,'" she replied.

"Oh, I get it! It relates to the comments your teachers made!"

"Right! It also stems from the environment. In kindergarten, we had a list of things to do, and we checked them off one by one. In network marketing, I have to-do lists and a schedule. It's also about the games we played, like follow the leader. I'm all about following the leader! In this industry, you can look back 40 years and see the strategies and building skills are still applicable today. Success leaves clues. There's always someone who has achieved what you want. All you have to do is follow what they did! Then the person who follows the leader the best gets to be the leader,"

Tina said. "I train people to be the leader of leaders."

"This is fascinating. Tell me more," Sara urged.

"Another game was show and tell. When you got picked, it was so exciting. You would research and prepare for it, then sit in front of the class and present it. Sara, that's a lot like what you have to do in every presentation: prepare, research, and put information together to share with others. It's show and tell, followed by kids who ask questions. To me, questions are like objections in sales. Answer those questions and you take care of the objections."

"You make it sound fun," Sara noticed.

"To me, it is," Tina replied. "Sara, do you remember there being star students when you were in school?"

"I sure do. Everyone wanted to be the star student!"

"I've found that people will do more for recognition than they will for money. You have to learn what people really want and then offer it to them in a fun way where everyone wins. People don't care about what you know until they know that you care," Tina said. "Those are the principles I use in network marketing, and they've served me well. More important, though, is that network marketing has served me well. It's given me an opportunity to be there for my son, and he is why I do what I do. Now, I get to help other people have what I have and learn how to do what I've done."

"That is so true, Tina. I'm divorced, and my daughter, Abby, is the reason for everything I do, too. She's the most important thing to me. Thankfully, Liz understands that," Sara said.

"Liz?" Tina asked.

"Oh, I'm sorry. I'm referring to Elizabeth Roberts; she's my employer," Sara said.

"You work for Liz? She's a great friend. I've known her for years," Tina exclaimed. "And you're right—she's one of the most understanding people I know. Liz understands that our kids are our priority. My lifestyle with my son always came first, and I built my business into it. I know that Liz has instilled that type of atmosphere at Roberts Development."

At that moment, Liz walked up.

"I thought I heard someone mention my name," she smiled. "I trust that you two have met. Actually, it looks like you're already great friends."

"I feel like we are," Sara answered. "Tina has a knack for making friends!"

"She's also got a knack for selling—she's one of the best I've ever had the pleasure to know," Liz commented. "Her network is quite impressive. In fact, I believe she knows most of the people here, and there are a *lot* of people here tonight."

"Well, I do recognize a few familiar faces," Tina grinned as she looked across the room.

"I was just telling Sara last week that it would benefit her to increase her network," remarked Liz.

"Is that so? Well, in that case, there's no time like the present," Tina said, grabbing Sara's arm as she whisked her toward a group of people in the middle of the room.

10

The Vision Creates Provision

Featuring Dr. Wendy Labat

Sara found that Tina was right. Not only was Liz understanding when she needed to take time away from work to be with her daughter, she often encouraged it. What surprised her most was that Liz was genuinely interested in Abby. She asked about her often, so much that Sara asked if she could bring her daughter to the office so she could meet her.

Abby and Liz hit it off right away. Someone who didn't know them would think they were grandmother and granddaughter from the way they talked and joked with each other. Liz often walked in with a gift for Abby, saying it caught her eye as she was shopping, and she thought of her.

Before long, Liz was inviting Sara and Abby to her home for Sunday brunch, and Sara reciprocated, inviting Liz to join them for Abby's birthday party. Sara didn't want Liz to feel obligated, but Liz really seemed to enjoy their time together and was often the one who reached out to them, asking if they were busy and wanted to go shopping or catch a movie.

Through it all, Sara never forgot to be grateful for her employer, who was investing not only in her growth, but in her daughter's life, as well.

Perhaps the greatest thing she had to be grateful for was that Liz included her in her personal and professional network, and it was a large network, indeed. Through Liz's network, Sara learned that there was much more to running a real estate development business than knowing real estate or development. To be successful, Liz needed connections in every realm—business, finance, health, marketing and sales, and a team of friends and advisors to support her.

Sara's circle widened a great deal. Through Roberts Development, she was introduced to people who had a wealth of experience. Her time spent with Liz away from work gave her the opportunity to know some of her employer's valued friends.

It was during a Saturday afternoon luncheon that she met Liz's longtime friend, Dr. Wendy Labat. As soon as they sat down, Dr. Wendy encouraged Sara to share her story, and when she was done, Sara turned the tables, asking Dr. Wendy to share a bit about herself.

"I've been an entrepreneur and business strategist for almost four decades. I'm also an international speaker with my own award-winning global streaming television show, Financial Cures with Dr. Wendy Labat. I've written two best-selling books as part of my Financial Cures Book Series," Dr. Wendy explained.

"Your own show? That sounds fascinating! So how did you

become a financial expert?"

"I started my entrepreneurial journey with no business experience and very limited resources. Back then, there was no Internet or social media and the only thing you could do with a cell phone was make an expensive phone call. Well, I did business with major corporations and government agencies. In order to be considered for the big contracts, you had to project a certain image, which meant having a brick-and-mortar office, employees, inventory on hand, and all the overhead that goes with it. If you projected anything less, you were perceived as a mom-and-pop operation not capable of handling big contracts.

"I projected that image for a while. Eventually, my company finances suffered from anorexic cashflow. I was forced to get creative. I had to make my money work for me and negotiate with my clients and vendors to get the terms and pricing I needed to not only stay in business but enhance the growth and development of my company.

"Some people might think that would discourage people from doing business with me, but it didn't. You see, there were benefits for doing business with female and minority-owned companies. Actually, it was mutually beneficial for me, my clients, and my vendors.

"It took a lot of work, Sara, but that experience taught me how to take control of my finances, make my money work for me, become a great negotiator, and a savvy entrepreneur. I started as a rookie entrepreneur with nothing, and I built a successful business and a sterling reputation," Dr. Wendy stated.

"It sounds like you've built an impressive career," Sara stated.

"Yes, I have, but that career has evolved over the years. When I married and started a family, I needed more personal and family time, so I opened a tax preparation business and then later expanded it to include insurance and financial services. Not wanting to be a hypocrite, I purchased the products and services I sold to my clients. A couple of years later, I was diagnosed with an aggressive form of breast cancer. Thank God I practiced what I preached. The cost to treat and conquer the disease was almost $1.5 million. My health insurance covered the entire cost. The supplemental coverages provided me with multiple six-figure tax-free financial shots in the arm. It was a blessing not having to worry about my business or money. I considered this the financial cure; hence The Financial Cures LLC was born, and I became The Financial Healer," Dr. Wendy said.

"I love the name and how you tied your circumstances into it," said Sara. "I admire people who can take adversity and turn it into something positive."

"Adversity is just a life lesson," Dr. Wendy said. "Even though it may not look like it at the time, in the end, you will realize that things happen for a reason, if only to make you stronger. I've had people say they've made a mistake or failed at something, and I always tell them that it's not a mistake or failure if they learn from it."

"You've definitely come out stronger! One day, I hope that I can say the same. I have to admit this has been a period of growth. Sometimes it's overwhelming, particularly with my finances. Not having a two-income household has been a struggle at times," Sara admitted.

"Sara, don't worry about provision. So many people think they have to wait until they have money to take action. I've had the most success when I've had the least amount of money. Don't worry about money, and don't do it for money," Dr. Wendy counseled.

"My life advice is to know that what God has in store for you is for *you*. His timing is always perfect. Just know that nobody can block your blessings but you. Follow the path the Spirit lights for you and do what the Spirit leads you to do, and everything will work out, Sara. No matter what the naysayers say, keep going. Remember, when He gives you the vision, He will give you the provision."

"I do believe I've been led to Liz for a reason," Sara said thoughtfully.

"Yes. Accept it and be open to learning from her. Be receptive to the advice people share, but make sure it's part of God's plan by tuning to the Spirit for affirmation. Be a person of your word and do things with integrity. This will take you places that money can't buy. I can testify to that!"

"I know I've met some incredible people through Liz, and I'm happy to say that you're one of them," Sara shared.

"Thanks, Sara! We meet the right people at the right place and at the right time. Things happen when and where they are supposed to. Even though it may not seem like it, your life changes and struggles can be a blessing. Take the good out of it and take what you've learned from those experiences and move forward. Garner the lessons because there is a lesson in every situation. If you don't learn the lesson, you'll keep repeating that class until you get a passing grade," Dr. Wendy laughed.

"That's fantastic advice, Dr. Wendy. Do you have any other nuggets of wisdom to share?" asked Sara.

"I do—perhaps the most profound is to expect nothing from man but expect everything from God. If you're expecting praise or rewards from man, you'll be disappointed most of the time. But if you expect nothing from man and expect your rewards from God, you'll be rewarded," Dr. Wendy advised.

"That's good. I like that perspective."

"I learned that from Joyce Meyer. Another thing she taught me is that whenever someone does you wrong, consider it a seed sown. You will reap a bountiful harvest as a result of it," Dr. Wendy shared.

"You are an insightful woman, Dr. Wendy," Sara reflected.

"I've learned a lot through the years. One of the main things experience has taught me is to do all I can do, let go of it and God will handle the rest."

"I need to remember that. So often, I struggle with letting go," Sara admitted. "I also have difficulty trusting myself to take risks now that I'm on my own. Oh, I do know that failure at some level is probably inevitable. But I prefer to play it safe."

"Oh, I know just the person who can help you overcome that! You have to meet my friend, Albert. If anyone can inspire you to take a leap, he can!" Dr. Wendy exclaimed.

"Who is Albert?"

"Albert Corey is my good friend. You know what, he's going to be in town at the end of the month. Let's set up a lunch. I'd love for you to meet him," Dr. Wendy invited.

The All-in Principle

Featuring Albert Corey

 As promised, Wendy introduced Sara to her friend, Albert Corey. From the moment they met and started talking, Sara felt like she was among friends. She loved his energy, his spontaneity, and his positivity.

Immediately, Albert wanted to hear her story. Giving him the abbreviated version, she walked him through her divorce, how she met Liz, and the time she had spent learning under Liz's wing.

"That brings us to the present. Now that I have a stable income, I'm thinking about investing some of the funds from the sale of my parents' house," informed Sara.

"Thinking about it? What's stopping you from just doing it?" he asked.

"Albert, like I told Dr. Wendy, I've never been a big risk taker, and to me, it's such a big risk. I have to think about my future, as well as my daughter," Sara stated.

"Sara, for 39 years, I've had an accounting and coaching business, working with 95,000 clients. All of that experience and expertise has taught me one thing—that most people are too cautious and scared of taking risks."

"And I can see why. I need a nest egg for reassurance. After all, I simply cannot afford to lose everything," Sara sighed.

"Or you could do the opposite," Albert suggested.

"Which is what?"

"Close your eyes and jump," he said.

"Excuse me?" she asked, not certain if she heard him correctly.

"Just close your eyes, jump off the cliff, and let it go," he said. "So many people are scared to spend money. They're scared to go to an event. They're scared to put themselves out there. What they don't know is that being overly cautious is what holds them back. I found that to be true time and time again. My business exploded when I stopped being scared—when I closed my eyes and took a giant leap without thinking about the risks or repercussions. I stopped thinking about why I shouldn't spend money and started to spend money without thinking about it at all."

"Wow. Weren't you a *little* scared?" she asked.

"Not after I saw the results. And I saw the results right away. I know it works. Sara, don't be afraid. Instead, be excited! I learned that if you're not ready to throw everything out to the wind, you can't be successful. I call it the all-in principle; you have to have all your chips all in—all of the time. Anything less and you're not fully committed to your success," he stressed.

"So, if I go all in, is there anything I can do to make sure I don't lose it all, to minimize the risk?"

"Yes, it's all about how you foster relationships with other people. You'll always need the support and advice of others. My advice to you is to remember the people you've met. Reach out to them and, whenever you can, help them remember you."

"Help them remember me? How can I do that? I've met a lot of people, but truthfully, I haven't had the opportunity to get to know all of them very well. I haven't done anything yet to stand out and be memorable," Sara remarked.

"Well, let me tell you how I did it. It's an interesting story. I think you'll like it," Albert said.

"I'm listening," Sara eagerly awaited.

"Again, it's about doing things without knowing the outcome beforehand. I met a man named Greg Reid at an event several years ago. Greg has mentored a lot of people, and he meets new people all the time. Believe me, he's well known and has a very wide circle. It's highly unlikely that he can possibly remember all of them all of the time. Anyway, after I met him, it was several years before I ran into him again. Now, I knew he didn't remember meeting me those years before. Why would he? So I walked up to him and did something out of the ordinary—totally out of the blue, I asked him what he drinks in the morning. He told me he drinks black coffee, with six sugars and nine creams. Sara, what do you think I gave him the next day?" Albert asked.

"You didn't," Sara grinned a knowing smile.

"I did. And he told me that I was the only person in his 20 years of mentoring and coaching who had ever asked what he wanted and actually took him seriously and brought it to him. The payoff was that four days later, I got a package in the mail containing three of his books and four of his tapes," Albert laughed. "And to this day, he reaches out to me every couple of weeks, sending me a text saying, 'Hey, Albert, how you doing?' Ever since then, we've been friends, and I can guarantee that Greg has not for one minute forgotten who I am."

"That's crazy," Sara said.

"Maybe, but the really crazy part is the coffee. Not many people would really believe that anyone would actually drink a cup of coffee with nine creams and six sugars!" he laughed.

"Seriously, though, it's about doing something extra and getting noticed, right?" Sara asked.

"Yes, that and going all in. I could have reached my hand out and reintroduced myself, hoping that this time he'd remember me. Instead, I went all in with the coffee and gave him everything he said he wanted. He didn't ask me to buy him a coffee. I did it because I wanted to. But I did it for a reason, because I learned that good things happen when I make people feel good."

"Let me guess—then people remember you and you get more clients?" Sara surmised.

"Let's just say that I've learned that when people make other people feel good, there are billions of dollars to be made. I built a successful tax office by making people feel good. It's called love marketing. My dad taught me that if you show people love, they'll come to you like there's no tomorrow," Albert shared.

"Albert, like your friend, Greg, I know that I'll never forget you. You've been incredibly helpful, and it's been a delight to talk to you," Sara said.

"I won't forget you, either. As a matter of fact, I'd like to pass on the gesture Greg sent to me. Look in the mail for some love," said Albert. "Hopefully, it will bring you success."

12

The Way You Play Games is the Way You Play Life

Featuring Billy Siordia

 Later that week, Sara smiled when she opened a thick padded envelope that was sent to her at Roberts Development. Inside was a book by Albert Corey, entitled *How to Grow Your Business While Drinking Coffee.* On the inside cover page was an inscription:

To my friend, Sara,

Coffee and success go together. Cheers to both!

Albert Corey

That kind gesture opened the door to communication and friendship. Sara found herself texting Albert as she read his book, pointing out excerpts that she thought were insightful and relevant to her. As time went on, she turned to Albert for advice and mentorship often. It was Albert who told her about an event, saying it was the event of the year and the talk of the town, perhaps the country. He shared information about his friend, Billy Siordia, who could provide her with the details and hopefully line her up with an exclusive invitation.

Albert sent the two a mutual email introduction, and Sara replied immediately. Anxiously awaiting a response, she was surprised when she got a phone call instead.

"Hi, Sara. This is Billy Siordia," he announced himself.

"What a pleasant surprise!" Sara exclaimed. "I'm so happy you called."

"Well, I thought it would be easier and more personal to talk directly with you," he said.

"It is. So Billy, our friend Albert told me you're directly involved with this exclusive event. I'd love to hear more. What can you tell me about it?" Sara asked.

"It's all about mentorship and personal and professional development. However, don't mistake this for your typical workshop or conference. It's a three-day event that is on an invitation-only basis. Actually, the event is the talk of the town but on a larger scale. Every year, we secure phenomenal speakers, including celebrities, Fortune 500 business owners and CEOs, and experts from different industries, who all share their success principles and secrets. But unlike other seminars and conferences, those who attend actually have access to these speakers and the opportunity to talk and mingle with all of them. It's fair to say that it is very relationship oriented. We aim to make it the one must-attend event of the year. And even if it doesn't seem possible, it gets even better and more exclusive every single year."

"Wow, that sounds absolutely incredible. I can understand why it's invitation only. So how does someone like me who isn't a business owner get in the door?" Sara asked.

"I'll start by telling you how I got involved. I started working with the founder of the event as a volunteer seven years ago. Today, I'm vice president of sales in his company," Billy said. "Before I met him, I was a sheet metal worker, believe it or not."

"How did you go from being a sheet metal worker to being VP of sales?" she said with obvious curiosity.

"I came into this position by playing games, literally."

"No kidding. How did that come about?" she asked.

"Well, when I first met my mentor, he taught me that how we play games is how we play life," Billy explained.

"That sounds interesting. Can you explain it to me?"

"As a sheet metal worker, I certainly wasn't an entrepreneur, and I didn't have money to invest in or start my own business. I wasn't in a position to even entertain entrepreneurship. My mentor taught me to volunteer and be of contribution, and that would position me to start making the money I needed to invest in my future," Billy said.

"When I first started as a volunteer, I worked for this event for free for six years. During that time, I built a relationship and bond with my mentor. I became a part of his family, and he brought me into his business and his home. I worked alongside him and, yes, we played pool, frisbee, chess, and other games. Today, I'm making good money working for him, and I have met some really incredible people," he said.

"He sounds a bit like my mentor, Liz. She makes me feel like I'm a valued part of her life," Sara shared.

"That's how it is. I met my mentor by going to events and helping out. Over time, we became friends and had fun together. Playing games became our pastime. Along the way, I learned that how we do one thing is how we do other things. It's about making the right decisions to stay on top of what you're doing and making those decisions wisely to make sure you're getting what you want out of it, as well," Billy explained.

"Did you ever think about the fact that how you play a game is how you go through life? Here's an example. Let's say you're playing chess. If you take a bold, wise, and risky move in the game of chess, you're probably more apt to take bold and risky moves in business and relationships. If you tend to cheat to gain an advantage, you're showing your opponent that you might cheat your customers or be a dishonest business owner. Your moves can lead to failure or complete success, and that applies to everything—games, business, life," Billy stated.

"I never thought of it that way! But you're right—we show our personality and values in everything we do, don't we?" she asked.

"Yes. Strategic moves show that you're a thinker and someone who is looking at the end goal. Spontaneous, impromptu moves reflect the opposite. The important thing to remember is if you make the right moves and keep faith, anything is possible. That's what happened for me. I made the right moves and contributed something of value to my mentor, and he was able to see that I had the character and initiative that he was looking for in his business," he shared.

"That's fantastic!" interjected Sara.

"It's all about understanding that anything is possible. You can start like me, with absolutely nothing and nobody around who can help you. Even with all that going against me, I was still able to achieve what I wanted. I learned that as long as I am knowledgeable, teachable, wise in making decisions, and caregiving, anything is possible. I'm living proof!" Billy explained.

"Well, I believe I am teachable and caregiving; I try to make good decisions, and I know I've learned a lot. I'm just starting out, Billy, and I think I can learn a lot from you. Besides, Albert said I have to attend your event if I want to learn from the best of the best. He also told me you could help me make that happen," Sara said.

"Are you willing to do whatever is needed to make it happen?" Billy asked.

"I sure am. If you need someone to set up chairs or to register people at the door, I'm your girl," she answered excitedly.

"I tell you what, I'll send you the details. Show up ready to contribute and be ready to play. When you do, you'll meet a lot of people who will have a tremendous impact on your future. Believe me, it is people and mentors like them that open up a whole new and exciting world, one that I know I wouldn't have ever had an opportunity to be part of if it hadn't been for my mentor. He taught me that I didn't have to have a college degree to be of value and have worth."

"Oh, I can relate to that," Sara stated.

"It's true. Sometimes, it's not what you know, Sara, but what you do and how you do it that first gets noticed. Do whatever you do with honesty, enthusiasm, and sincerity, and you'll find that doors open for you. Before long, it'll be you who is giving another person an opportunity that they wouldn't have had before they met you."

"That would be amazing. And, Billy, I can't tell you how happy I am that we had this talk. Even more, I'm super excited about meeting you and doing whatever it takes to be a part of this event. I've heard nothing but awesome things about it!" Sara exclaimed.

"It's the best of the best, Sara. Come ready to play, and you'll be amazed at what you'll learn," Billy said.

"Oh, I will. You can expect to see me bright and early and ready to go," she said, before another thought entered her mind. "Oh, and before I forget, Billy, what do you like to drink first thing in the morning?" she asked, with a smile he couldn't see over the phone, but one she thought he'd return when they met in person.

To Achieve Abundance, Create Value

Featuring Paul Hutchinson

Two months later, Sara walked into the resort where the event was being held and immediately purchased two drinks, one for herself and one for Billy, who graciously enjoyed her gift for a few minutes before stating that there was a lot of work to be done. Not letting the opportunity go to waste, she eagerly asked what she could do to help.

They spent the morning setting up tables and chairs and organizing programs and agendas. Then they unboxed hundreds of books, authored not only by the featured speakers, but also by many of the guests who would be attending. Fascinated by the topics, Sara admired the book covers and read the synopsis and author biography of every single book.

"I want to read every one of them!" she exclaimed.

"Me, too," Billy replied. "Over the years, I've built quite a collection of books from attending this event. The awesome part is that you'll be able to meet all of the authors — that's a cool bonus. Right now, though, let's finish setting up. We've only got another hour or so before we're done. Then, you'll have the rest of the day to enjoy the resort."

A couple hours later, Sara took a dip in the pool and soaked up some sun as she lounged in the tropical oasis atmosphere. She was left feeling rested, relaxed, and at the same time, excited for the event to begin the next day.

In the morning, she found herself sitting in the audience of Paul Hutchinson, one of the event's featured speakers who had come highly recommended by Billy. From the moment he stepped on stage, his energy captured Sara, but it was his message that truly resonated with her.

Paul introduced himself as the founder of a multi-billion-dollar investment fund who was committed to philanthropy and active in renowned charities. After sharing his background, Sara realized that he was not only one of the most accomplished people she had ever encountered, but also one of the most consistently giving and charitable individuals she had ever met. Amazingly, rather than crediting his giving nature to his wealth, he did the opposite and credited his wealth to his giving nature.

His speech was short, but it struck home and was so powerful that Sara found herself taking notes, hoping to capture every word.

"A man by the name of Paul Piltzer was one of my mentors, and he played a role in my philosophy about money. He explained to me that the challenge with most people is they misunderstand money and wealth. They believe we live in a zero-sum world. To them, if someone wants a million dollars, someone else has to give up a million dollars. I'm here to tell you that is not true.

"The problem comes from the definition of economics, which defines it as 'the division of scarce resources.' Today, that definition of economics precludes us from understanding the truth, which is that we don't live in a world of scarce resources. No, we live in a world of abundance. When you understand that, you can create a business that is a win-win-win. It's a win for your customers, for you, and for everyone involved. Every one of us lives a lifestyle that is comparable to kings and princes of old. Today, those who have the least still have far more than the most powerful and elite of centuries past. That is because kings were rulers, and they took care of only themselves, leaving a society of scarce resources. However, true, lasting wealth depends on the belief that we live in abundance, and there is enough abundance to go around for everyone. You can understand it from this principle:

"There are ten men on an island. Every day, they go fishing to catch fish to feed their families. They catch just enough to feed their families, so everyone is happy. Then, two men are entrepreneurs, and they come up with an idea to make a net. At night, they stitch and weave until they've created a large intricate net. Then they go out and use that net to catch enough fish to feed the entire island. That's good, right?

"Now, the problem at this point is when two out of ten men are doing the work, that leaves 80 percent unemployment, and a dysfunctional society would tax these two men 80 percent of their fish and allow the other eight men to sit around and do nothing. A well-functioning economy, on the other hand, would encourage the other men to contribute. One would get better at building boats, one would get better at building houses, and one would get better at educating the children. They would each learn a craft and contribute toward not only their own wellbeing, but the wellbeing of everyone on the island. The lifestyle as a whole would improve dramatically because of the ingenuity of those two men. That's the world we live in today. Every single new invention and improvement has the capability of creating unlimited wealth for the world as we know it. When you understand that, you can come up with ideas and solutions that create wealth for you and your family, your employers, and your customers. It can be a win-win-win without anyone having to lose.

"Remember," Paul concluded, "if you want to become a millionaire, you have to create a million dollars of value for the world. If you want to be a billionaire, create a billion dollars of value for the world."

Sara was fortunate to be able to meet Paul personally after the event. She was in a group of six attendees who gathered around him to ask questions, and he was generous when asked to elaborate on his principles.

"I made a decision early in my career that 20 percent of my income and 20 percent of my time would be invested toward making a significant impact in the lives of others. When that happens, your financial success will be unlimited.

"You can call it universe, God, or whatever you want," he continued. "The truth is there is a powerful force that is very interested in us doing good and giving back. In doing so, amazing things start to happen.

"Let me ask, how does someone become a founder or partner of a

26-billion-dollar investment fund? As a university dropout, the statistical probability that I would be in that position is basically zero. The only way I can understand it is that I made that commitment to donate 20 percent when I was younger.

"I decided my charitable focus would revolve around children. I joined several children's charity boards, and I was on the Make A Wish Board of Directors for more than seven years. I've received amazing personal, spiritual, and financial fulfillment from those efforts. In fact, a lot of the ultra-high net worth investors I've met and worked with came from relationships I developed in some of those charitable pursuits."

Immediately, Sara was impressed with Paul's dedication and commitment to children.

"Can I ask how you got to a place where you could afford to give 20 percent and spend so much time and money on such worthwhile causes?" she asked.

"Early on in my career, a mentor told me that the most valuable piece of real estate I would ever own was the six inches between my ears. By developing that, he said I would have infinite success. Now, let me clarify; that education doesn't have to be in brick-and-mortar schools. He suggested that the best education was from mentors, so that is what I recommend you do, Sara. They don't have to be people who are physically in front of you. Find people who have the fruit on the tree and have written books and created audio programs—people who have been successful in business, finance, leadership, and relationships. Then turn your car into a university on wheels! That's what I did. I bought a Range Rover that used to belong to LeBron James, and it had a $60,000 audio system in it, but I never used the sound system for any purpose other than improving my mind and increasing my knowledge.

"If you read a book once a month, in three months, nobody will know that you've done it. In three years, some people close to you will know because they'll notice changes in you. In thirty years, most people will know that you've read a book a month because by that time, you'll have made a significant impact on the world."

"That's incredible, Paul. And I hope one day that I'm in a position to make the type of impact on others that you're making," Sara said.

"Don't wait for one day—you can begin to make a positive and powerful difference today. When you do, that's when your life will change," he encouraged.

You Can Do Hard Things

Featuring Cynthia Caughie

 Sara met a new friend late that afternoon. It was during social hour that they found themselves sitting next to each other.

"Hi, I'm Cynthia Caughie," she smiled and extended her hand.

After introductions were made, Cynthia asked Sara about her background.

"Well, it's not a long or interesting story. I work for an incredible woman who owns a real estate development company. It's actually my first job after spending more than a decade married and raising my daughter. I'm learning so much, but I know that I'm at a point where it's time for me to take real action toward a career and a future that will provide stability for us. But it's not easy to know what to do and if it's right. Now it's your turn, Cynthia. What do you do?"

"I am a mom of three lovely ladies. I also own a restaurant, and I am an entrepreneur and in real estate. Oh, and I wrote a book," Cynthia smiled.

"What is the name of the book?" Sara asked.

"It's called *YOU Can Do Hard Things.* It's a self-development book, and I think it can help you with those decisions you need to make," Cynthia said.

"Then I definitely will make sure to read it. What kind of restaurant do you own, Cynthia?" Sara asked.

"I own Homerun Pizza. You might have heard of it?" Sara asked with a smile.

"I sure have! My daughter loves it! She'll be impressed that I met you," Sara announced. "You are so accomplished. One day, I'd like to tap into that level of success. Yet, I don't know where to start. Based on your experience, what is the most important thing I should focus on at this part of my life?"

"Growth. I always say to be proactive with your growth, not reactive with your life," Cynthia told her.

"Oh, that's poster worthy," Sara mused. "It just seems like I get overwhelmed, not knowing if I'm making the right decisions or not. I'm getting better about moving out of my comfort zone, but there are times when I feel like lack of experience puts me at a disadvantage."

"I don't totally agree. You're in a position where you have a world of possibilities ahead of you. Aaah, to be free to roam about with no worries of what's next. To start from the new place of the first steps. You are the holder of the pen, and you get to write your own story. What adventures will you go on today? How will you decide? What will spark your attention? Who will you meet? How will they interact with you? Will they change your world forever? The endless possibilities of wonder are exciting. It all starts with YOU!"

"I wish I had your enthusiasm," Sara admitted.

"Oh, you can do hard things; it's about your beliefs," Cynthia shared.

"My first encounter with beliefs and how to outline them was so eye opening and a little scary, honestly, but I'd like to tell you they don't have to be. There are so many instances where people give others permission to have a voice in their lives, when really, we should be confident enough in our own skin to make all our own decisions and to make them with the belief and confidence of certainty. These are all very powerful words. Why do I tell you this? Well, because no one taught me how to do this. I learned from my own experiences that there is a way to be so filled with joy that it's pretty much foolproof of self-doubt.

"I tell you what, Sara, come sit with me and let's have a glass of wine! Do you like wine? I'm from wine country so it's really like water to me," Cynthia invited.

As they lingered over a glass of Chardonnay, Sara learned more about her new friend.

Most of all, she enjoyed her enthusiasm and the energy in which she shared her information.

"Now for the best thing I ever learned. Ready! Wait, do you have a pen and paper to write this down!" Cynthia laughed. "I'm kidding, but seriously, this is so good I don't want you to forget it. CONFIDENCE IS WORTH MORE THAN MONEY! There is no better currency than to be rich with confidence. When you have confidence, you can rule the world. I mean, think about it. What does it take to wear a string bikini when you haven't tanned since last year? Confidence! What does it take to write a book? Confidence! What does it take to walk into a room, shoulders back, lipstick on, and a smile that brightens the whole room? Confidence. You get the picture, cutie?"

"I'm starting to," Sara laughed, enjoying Cynthia's personality and style.

"Sara, you can have read every book and be the smartest teacher in the room, but if you don't have the confidence to write a paper and voice your opinion, what's it really worth? You can love everyone you meet, but when THE ONE comes into your life, if you can't talk to him, how will he even know you are alive? Confidence is the power that makes you take action. You will make decisions quicker with confidence. You will love yourself the best with a confident heart. You can share your vision, your optimism, and your words to anyone who will listen when you have confidence.

"Do you hear what I'm saying? Confidence is just about as illustrious as winning the lottery. If I could just give it to you, I would. BUT I can't. It's up to you. You can build your confidence, though. Want to hear how?"

"If you can tell me, that would be awesome!" Sara answered.

"Sara, I don't know you well, but I promise you can do hard things. It wasn't easy to get a divorce, but you did it and came out okay, right? It's not easy being a single mom, but you're rocking it, right? It's not easy reentering the workforce after a decade away from it, but look at you—you're doing it! See, you can do hard things, and the more confidence you have and the more confidence you build, the more things you'll be able to do that you never thought you could do before," Cynthia shared.

"Looking at it that way, you might be right," Sara said.

"Oh, I am right. Believe in yourself. Believe you have everything you need inside of you. You've got this, and it all stems from your beliefs. Sure, this has been a big turning point for you. You're figuring out who you are, and that's such an amazing time and opportunity for you. And this is an opportunity for me to help you. Here," Cynthia said, reaching into her bag and pulling out a book. "This is a copy of my book as a reminder that you can do hard things. And if you ever doubt that you can, turn to it and remind yourself before you let amazing opportunities pass you by."

"Thank you so much!" Sara exclaimed. "Not only have you been a huge confidence booster, but you've been awesome to talk to. I will remember your encouragement and confidence in me."

"Please do. I believe in you, Sara. It's time for you to believe in yourself," Cynthia smiled before reaching over to give her new friend a hug of support.

$$\textbf{15}$$

Live Your Legacy While You're Building It

Featuring Jen Du Plessis

 The next morning, Cynthia was waiting for her when she walked into the room.

"Oh, there you are! I'm so glad I caught you! I wanted to introduce you to my great friend, Jen Du Plessis. Jen is one of those people you won't ever forget!" exclaimed Cynthia. "After hearing your story yesterday, I just knew you had to talk with her."

After grabbing a coffee, they sat at a table in the lobby and talked.

"Cynthia speaks so highly of you, Jen. I'd love to hear your story," Sara smiled.

"Where do I start?" Jen asked. "How about at the beginning? I spent most of my life proving, and not living. I felt the need to prove to people that I was worthy. I was called 'Jenny who ain't got a penny.' My uncle told me I would amount to nothing. I knew that if I grew up without changing something, I'd end up like my parents. We didn't have a lot of money, my father was an alcoholic and my mother was a verbal abuser. So, I carried a penny around in my shoe just to show everyone I *had* a penny!"

"So you had to prove that you could earn money?" Sara asked.

"My uncle told me I was going to be just like my parents, so I did everything I could to prove him wrong. It wasn't just about having money; it was being successful in everything! I was the best at everything I could possibly be. In fact, I was attempting to be perfect. In my mind, if I was perfect, the people around me would see my changes and see that I could achieve many successes. I hoped that my accomplishments would make them proud. During this time, I waited for someone to give me praise, any kind of praise; but I only got crickets."

"That's sad," Sara said.

"At the time, it was. But that changed later in my adult years. I had become very successful, but I was working like a dog. One evening at dinner with my family while I was outside of the restaurant working again, I'd had enough! I knew there has to be a better way, so I set out on a mission to do what I called 'cracking the code,'" Jen said.

"Were you able to crack the code?" Sara asked.

"I did. I came up with five very specific strategies to crack the code. As a result, I created twice the results in half the time. I now call it Living a Luxury Lifestyle, which is about taking care of ourselves first, having the luxury of spending time with our families, creating memories and experiences; and then taking care of our business. Most people have this backwards. If you look at the wheel of a car, the wheel is steel and strong, and most make this their priority. They work so hard to make their business strong and healthy, but on the outside, the tire, or in this case, their personal lives, are in bad shape. The tire is worn, has no tread, and there are nails in it. My goal, Sara, is to invert this and focus on the steel being their personal lives and tire their business. I know people can have a big, beautiful business when they have more daily focus, while being as good to themselves as they are to their business. This sometimes means saying yes to themselves and no to their clients."

"And you made this strategy a business?" Sara asked.

"Yes, that's what I do. I used to feel like I was eating soup with a fork: exhausted every day, living in chaos, laten with excuses, and doing activities that weren't moving me or my business forward; I simply wasn't fulfilled. Today I'm committed to helping others stop eating soup with a fork, too. We address both mindset and mechanics, or strategies, and help people create a beautiful life where they *still* kick ass in business. I help them realize that they can actually live their legacy while they're building it. They don't have to wait! When they learn to work on purpose, they can then play with passion. I want them to have the best of both worlds *today*, not tomorrow," Jen explained.

"That sounds like an awesome way to live ... and work," Sara remarked.

"It is. It's very tactical, and it's very mindful. I went from 'Jenny who ain't got a penny,' to Jenny who has plenty of pennies, but that's not what's important. What *is* important is that I went from Proving to Living!" Jen replied.

"How would I start to implement Living a Luxury Lifestyle in my life?" asked Sara.

"The first thing you need to do is to find your inspiration. Don't find what motivates you because that is short lived. It wanes over time, and you always need more. As a result, you never get anything done because you're always needing outside stimulation to achieve your goals. There's really no action taking place. Instead, find what *inspires* you because inspiration gives you that invisible push that will help you grow and keeps you going," Jen said.

"That makes sense," Sara agreed. "What's next?"

"You have to identify your core values, Sara, because those are the things you'll go to when you're making decisions. You can follow your gut or intuition, but it's really great if you can use your values when making decisions. For instance, if one of your values is family, why would you be working until eleven o'clock at night? Why are you not showing up to the baseball game or the recital? If your value is financial stability, why are you constantly buying shiny objects, that magic pill to help you succeed? Do you understand what I'm saying?" asked Jen.

"I sure do," Sara nodded.

"Okay, let's move on. The third thing is determining what fulfills you. Think about what makes you smile! If it's spending time with your family, then how do you get more of it? How do you make them first? For me, dancing makes me smile, so I determined how to get more of that. If it's as simple as sitting and having a cup of coffee in the morning and listening to the birds sing, how do you get more of that? When you know what fulfills you, that will inspire you! Inspiration is your why—why do you do this every day? The 'what' is what you are doing, and the 'how' is how you are going to accomplish it. Those three things are how I help my clients increase their awareness for what they really want," Jen said. "Once they're clear on that, they can start to move forward with other things. But first, they have to get really, really clear on what they want."

"I think that can be tough sometimes. People think they know what they want, but they might not really know. Am I right?" Sara interjected.

"Oh, yes, that's why I have clients focus on these things first. I want them to have a deep and honest conversation with themselves, so they really know what inspires them and what they want. Otherwise, they won't have the inspiration to make it happen," Jen offered.

"My advice to find out what fulfills you is to slow down long enough to take time with yourself, brainstorm, breath and assess, so you can then speed up, instead of speeding up to slow down," Jen added. "And don't forget to put yourself first, before your job or your career. It's about loving yourself. My mom used to live by a quote by Ella Wheeler Wilcox that I think is so fitting: 'We flatter those we scarcely know. We please the fleeting guest; And deal many a thoughtless blow to those who love us best.'"

"I love that! It's so true."

"It is, and I was guilty of it. I was flattering everybody and making everyone else happy, but I was dealing all these thoughtless blows to people I loved the best, including myself. That's why I know how important it is to be as good to yourself as you are to your business," Jen admitted. "What I set out to do in the real world, as I am here in talking with you, is to acknowledge that I had catching up to do. Let me explain. I had actually been on vacation with my family and couldn't even remember the vacation even occurred! Oh, I had catching up to do! And I thought if I can share how not to do that with people like you so you can have the years that I'm trying to catch up and make up, it will bring me all the joy in the world."

"That's so unselfish of you, Jen."

"Well, I've learned it's not worth the sacrifice. Being present is what is important. It's not what you did for a living that's important to your family—it's who you are," Jen said.

"I've struggled with that as a mother, especially now that I'm divorced and working full time," Sara admitted.

"Just remember it's important to be there for your child. There is more to life than having a business. Knowing that, your business can still be incredible. I promise that you're not going to sacrifice your business. My clients have actually found that by taking care of themselves, they double and triple their business! On the other hand, if you neglect yourself, your business will sacrifice you. And I don't want that to happen to you, Sara," Jen explained.

Just then, Cynthia interjected, reminding them that the conference was beginning, and they needed to get to their seats.

"If you're like me, Sara, you can talk to Jen all day, but we do need to get moving," she said.

"I could," Sara laughed. "But you're right ... we are cutting it close. I don't want to walk in a minute late."

"Don't worry," Jen said. "Remember, I was the woman who couldn't slow down. They used to call me 'Speedy Delivery.' Just follow me; I'll get us there quickly!"

(16)

Invest in Yourself

 Not only did Sara leave the event with a dozen books to read, but she had also formed connections and friendships with some of the other attendees. As she learned about their lives and routines, she found a common thread among them—they all made time for themselves in different ways. Some avidly practiced yoga, while others preferred meditation. There were joggers, a woman who was training for her first marathon, and even a gentleman who had completed three triathlons in the last two years.

Realizing that she hadn't seen the inside of a gym since she took an aerobics class after Abby was born, Sara knew that she'd neglected herself over the years. As a full-time mother and housewife, her family's needs had been a priority, and she simply didn't have time to put herself first. But now that Abby was older and spending equal time with her father, Sara didn't have any excuses and knew it was time to invest in herself.

When she started working at Roberts, she received a folder explaining employee benefits, and she thought she recalled one of the perks being a discount on a gym membership. Pulling it out, she skimmed through the pamphlet: optional insurance, financial and retirement counseling, identity theft protection, and, ah, there it was, a 20 percent discount on a one-year membership at the local fitness club.

As she was looking at it, Liz peeked into her office.

"Sara, we're ordering lunch in today. Do you want anything?" she asked.

"Thanks, but no thanks. I'm good," Sara answered.

"Nonsense. You have to eat. With the Phillips deal coming up, you're going to need all the energy you can get," her employer said.

"Oh, don't I know it," laughed Sara. "But I actually thought I'd use my lunch hour to sign up at the fitness club. I can grab something on my way back."

"Good for you!" Liz shared her approval. "And don't worry if you need a few extra minutes. The Phillips project will still be here when you get back."

A trainer at the fitness club gave Sara a full tour of the facilities, a locker, and a printout of their regular classes and other amenities. Before returning to the office, she stopped at the juice bar and ordered a smoothie and a salad to go.

Back at the office, she ate at her desk, while going through the checklist for the items they still needed for the Phillips closing. It was a complex project with a lot of moving pieces and parties. Corporate buyers usually had multiple people involved, from boards of directors to CEOs, to accountants and attorneys. Given that the parameters of the property and the plans for development had expanded since the initial offer was accepted, the project had required multiple revisions and amendments. Making sure that the proper paperwork was in order and reflected the most current information had been Sara's job. And Liz was right—it definitely kept her busy.

She still made time to get to the fitness club three times a week. Initially, she thought a new fitness regimen would leave her tired, but she was surprised that she was actually more energized on the days when she worked out. And as she stuck with it, she was pleased to find that the workouts became easier. She also found that her membership was having a positive impact on Abby, who was enjoying her mother's newfound fondness for healthier foods, particularly smoothies.

It wasn't long before Abby was making her own smoothies and experimenting by adding different fruits and, surprisingly, vegetables. She was so impressed with herself that she invited her friends over one Saturday afternoon to sample the different flavors.

"I wish I'd known years ago that all it took to get her to eat vegetables was to blend them with strawberries and bananas," Sara told Liz and Shannon. "I'm not kidding—it used to be a nightmare just getting her to take a thank-you bite! Now, she *asks* me if we have any raw carrots or spinach, insisting that her smoothie won't be the same without it!"

"It sounds like she's really into it, but tell me, are her smoothies good?" Liz asked.

"Yes, they are. As a matter of fact, I think they're just as good as the club's smoothies — at least they would be if she could get them to the right consistency. Apparently, our blender isn't quite as powerful as professional juice machines, as she's reminded me more than a few times when she talks about opening her own juice bar, but it'll do for now."

For the next few weeks, Sara faithfully attended the fitness club, carrying her gym bag on the train with her in the morning and returning with it in the evening. It wasn't long before she made a couple friends and had a favorite instructor, making her look forward to her workouts even more. She hadn't missed a day until Liz notified her that the Phillips closing had been rescheduled.

"I know it's not going to be easy, but we need to make sure we don't overlook anything. We all need to work together to make sure this goes off without a single glitch," she'd said.

Sara worked through her lunch and after hours every day, preparing documents and double and triple checking that every detail in the agreements and addendums was in order.

"We're ready," she told Liz the afternoon before the closing.

"Thank you, Sara. I know how hard you've worked on this project. You haven't even taken time to go to the gym, have you?" Liz asked.

"No, I haven't. To be honest, I think I've gotten a better workout here this week!" she laughed.

The closing was scheduled for the next morning, and hoping that everything had gone smoothly, Sara and her coworkers anxiously awaited Liz's arrival. As soon as she walked in the door, Liz announced, "Thanks to all of you, our biggest and most complex project to date went off flawlessly. I know how much hard work and dedication everyone put into it. That's why I'm closing the doors at noon and giving everyone the afternoon off. You deserve it!"

Late that morning, Liz asked Sara what her plans were for the afternoon.

"I think I'm going to get in an afternoon workout. It might do me good to burn off some stress," Sara smiled.

"I know it's been hectic around here, but you stepped up to the plate, Sara, and I appreciate that. You really have come a long way since you started working here, and I've come to depend on you quite a bit. I wanted to give you something to thank you," Liz said, passing an envelope to Sara.

"What's this?"

"Just a token of my appreciation. Oh, and here's something for Abby, too," she said, reaching under her desk to pick up a large gift bag.

"That's not necessary, Liz, but you and I both know that Abby will love it, whatever it is," she smiled. "But seriously, it's not a puppy or a guinea pig or anything like that, is it?"

"Not at all," Liz laughed. "Let's just say that I thought I'd give Abby a head start on her latest venture."

After enjoying her first workout in ten days, Sara retrieved her bags from her locker and walked the two blocks to the train station. Sitting the gift bag on the empty seat beside her, she opened Liz's envelope, which contained a handwritten note on her elegantly monogramed stationery.

Sara,

Thank you for your dedication to our success. As a token of my appreciation, please accept my invitation to be my guest at this year's Elite Health Summit, all expenses paid, of course. I applaud your dedication to your health and our company.

Your friend,

Liz

Sara was once again grateful for the day that she met Liz and the impact the woman had made on not just her life, but also Abby's. Peering into the gift bag on the seat beside her, she gently moved the tissue paper aside to get a glimpse of what Liz was giving her daughter, and when she saw the box, a smile spread across her face. Abby was getting her very own professional juicer.

17

The More You Give,
the More You Get

Featuring Mike Berkowitz

 With the Phillips project behind them, everything went back to business as usual at Roberts Development. Knowing that she had played a valuable role in its success did wonders for Sara's confidence, and she was soon looking forward to new challenges that would push her limits and expand her knowledge.

Her recent interest in improving her health and fitness was also new and exciting. Her original motive had been to tone and tighten the muscles that had slacken over time, hoping to prevent the thickening of the waist that her mother and grandmother had both experienced in middle age. However, as she evolved, so did her purpose for working out. She wanted to be around for a long time and hoped that she would be as active as Liz when she was in her sixties.

It was Liz who explained to her that the health and fitness of her employees was important to her as a business owner. Not only did it keep costs and absenteeism to a minimum, but she found that the more she invested in her employees' health, the more she got back in return. "Creating positive habits and a disciplined mindset is so beneficial, and exercise is a great way to achieve it," she'd said.

Sara loved the fact Liz supported her employees' fitness. To be invited to attend the healthcare summit with her was an honor. Not only did she get to spend a few days with her employer and friend, but it was also like a mini vacation, especially since Liz took care of her transportation and accommodations.

The venue for the summit was breathtaking. The five-star hotel was strategically built at the foot of a mountainous backdrop that she could look at all day, given the opportunity. Once inside, there was a level of grandeur to the architecture, but also the décor. From the plush carpet underfoot to the opulent oversized chandeliers that glistened overhead, every item was specifically chosen to complement the others. Together, they all made a subtle, but oh so obvious statement.

"Oh, look, Sara," Liz nudged her arm when they entered the conference room later that morning. "There's my friend, Mike. Let's go say hello before he's surrounded by a ton of people. He's quite popular, you know."

"Mike, it's so good to see you! We haven't talked since—well, just how long has it been?" Liz exclaimed when they approached the gentleman.

"Too long," Mike answered, reaching out to give Liz a hug. "And I see you brought a friend…"

"Oh, yes. Sara, this is my friend, Mike Berkowitz. He's well respected in the healthcare industry, I assure you. Mike, this is my friend, Sara Andrews, who is also a valuable employee, I might add," Liz said. "For the next two days, though, I just want her to relax and enjoy this experience. The summit is one of the most informative and enjoyable events I attend every year."

"I wholeheartedly agree with you, Liz," Mike said. "It's one of the reasons I go out of my way to make it every year."

"I'm glad Liz invited me to tag along," said Sara. "So far, it's lived up to the hype. From the minute we got into the car, I've enjoyed every minute. So, Mike, how did you get here? Did you fly?"

"If you're talking about travel, yes, I flew in this morning. But it's a different story if you're talking about how I got to be one of the presenters at the largest healthcare summit in the country," he answered.

"Oh, do tell," Sara said.

"Well, I got here from a very interesting place, I assure you. To explain, I'll have to start at the beginning. I started a company called Pacific Stem Cells, which provided stem cells to the stars and some very well-known celebrities. Before I owned that company, I owned another company called Telehealth Care, which was a video medicine company that I later sold," explained Mike.

"That sounds really interesting," Sara mentioned.

"Interesting? It's fascinating," Liz interjected. "Mike, do share your story. I never tire of hearing it."

"At the time that I started Telehealth Care, video medicine was a new concept, and I was motivated to create it for my son, who had autism and learning challenges when he was a kid. So I built the program for him, and it was working very well. But I was also working as a contractor, setting up media servers in Afghanistan, and I got injured from shrapnel. I was just there to save lives and make money to pay for the services my son needed, and I ended up wounded. But when I came back, nothing in Western medicine worked for me," he admitted.

"That's terrible," Sara interjected.

"It was at the time, but it led me to something greater. In my quest for treatment that worked, I turned to an experimental, holistic approach to healing. That's when I found stem cells, which absolutely healed me. A few days later, when my pain was gone, the first thing I did was give the treatment to my son, and I was amazed at how well it worked. He was 100 percent normal," Mike explained.

"How incredible!" exclaimed Sara.

"It is. I knew right then and there that it was a life-changing procedure, and I vowed to bring stem cells to the world, even though people told me not to. After all, I had a very successful telehealth company that was creating an incredible profit. But I knew that stem cells were my future. And, Sara, I knew I did the right thing because it quickly became apparent that the rewards I get for treating people are far better than money. I've learned that helping someone in such a profound way is absolutely the best thing you can do for someone. My experience has taught me that when you really heal and repair someone, it is the biggest and highest honor. So, Sara, when you asked me how I got here, there was no way I could give you the condensed version. I got here because I was hurt and because I knew what pain was like. I was suffering, and so was my son. Stem cells got me here," he said.

"That's phenomenal!" Sara replied.

"I can vouch for Mike's stem cell treatments," Liz interjected. "I've benefited from them, as well. As a matter of fact, they saved me from needing knee replacement surgery. I have Mike to thank for that."

"The reward is why I do this. It's a success at a different level than what I've ever experienced. And I have to say that it has taught me so much. I learned that the more I give, the more I get. I've made a practice of doing two free cases a month, because I know there is no better feeling than doing what I love and seeing how it changes lives. For example, there was one man who was suffering from extensive Parkinson's disease, and I treated him for free—in front of a group of physicians who were skeptical, at best. The only thing I asked for in return was a couple referrals … if the stem cell treatment worked. Two weeks later, I received unlimited referrals. The moral of the story is when you do good work, good things happen—big things. And it all came from a place of love because I wanted to get my son and my wife back."

"And to think it all started because you got wounded in Afghanistan," Liz commented.

"I guess you could say I turned a lemon into lemonade," Mike smiled.

"You sure did! You were fortunate, and your story is quite unique. I know it's a success story that won't be forgotten," Liz stated. "Sara, Mike is a perfect example of how success can come in different, even unexpected ways. No two success stories are alike, which is why I encourage you to talk to people from all industries and walks of life. You never know where you'll find your inspiration and the success principles that will guide you toward the future you want."

"Liz is right. The people you meet on your journey will have an amazing impact on you. I know. I've treated small children, grandparents, and friends. I've also treated doctors, politicians, professional athletes, and actors. And I can honestly say it was an honor to treat every one of them. Like I said, it's not the money that matters the most. It's the relationships that are created along the way. It's very fascinating how in-depth that relationship becomes. Don't get me wrong—it's not an interactional relationship. It's transactional, which is a very high level of communication and trust. That's what allows me to be here doing what I do today."

"Are you presenting at the summit, Mike?" Sara inquired.

"Oh, yes. You just got the back story, but I'll be sharing information on how stem cell treatments work, and you'll watch videos showing actual patients before and after treatment. I think you'll find it interesting," Mike said.

"I already do!" Sara said. "One day, Mike, I hope to be successful enough to make such a positive difference in other people's lives."

"You will. You just have to find the niche that makes you feel good and transforms your life. It's something I learned from Dr. Pallos, a famous neurosurgeon who took me under his wing and, so very patiently, taught me how to help my patients and their families. This surgeon showed me how to really resonate with my patients. In other words, he taught me how to be so connected to my patients that when they feel good, I feel just as good. When you're at the level where you can do good things for people and that makes you feel as good, if not better than it does them, that's when you've discovered your true purpose and the richest rewards."

"Well, I do know how I'd like to give to others and make their lives better. Now, I just need to find a way to do it," Sara shared.

"If you know, you will find a way. You're fortunate to have a remarkable mentor. Liz has provided me with encouragement, support, and friendship throughout the years. I'm sure she's just as valuable, if not more, to you," replied Mike.

"That is true. And just like you, Mike, Liz and I wouldn't have met if it weren't for some unfortunate circumstances that led to an unexpected train ride," Sara said. "Because of a lost train ticket, I've met some truly remarkable people. It's given me so much already, but like you said, it seems the more it gives, the more I get."

(18)

Seem on Point

Featuring Eric Stuerken

 At lunch, they were joined by another one of Liz's friends.

"Hello, ladies, is this seat taken?" he asked, motioning toward an empty chair.

"It is now. Eric, there's always room at my table for you," Liz said, jumping up to hug the newcomer.

"Sara, this is my very good friend, Eric Stuerken. Eric, Sara is one of my assistants ... and also a great friend," Liz shared.

"Do you know anyone who isn't a good friend, Liz?" asked Eric.

"Not yet," Liz laughed.

"It's nice to meet you, Eric. Liz has certainly introduced me to some amazing people. So, tell me, what is it that you do?" Sara asked.

"Well, my core business is called Better Qualified, a company that specializes in business and consumer credit. What does that mean? We build, fix, and monitor it. I cofounded the company 16 years ago. But I've recently started another business in a totally different industry, which is why I'm here at the health summit," he replied.

"What's that?"

"It's called One Minute Before. It's a fitness app for corporate wellness," Eric said.

"How does a guy who is in the credit business start a fitness app?" Sara asked.

"Well, I'm a big fitness advocate. I believe that your morning routine structures the rest of the day. As long as you do something physical in the morning, you're set up for the rest of your day. Knowing that, I created an app that promotes fitness in the workplace."

"Oh, I remember Liz talking about starting that at Roberts Development! Can you tell me a little bit about it?"

"I'd love to. The app tells you to do an exercise every hour on the hour for one minute. At the end of the exercise minute, you enter the total reps. If you have a smartwatch, it also tracks your vitals while you're doing the exercise. We've launched it for corporate employees. So many are working from home now, and they aren't able to go to the gym, and this app helps keep them active and fit," Eric explained. "It's incredibly easy—each notification has a video that shows you how to do the one-minute exercises. With this app, there is no equipment required and there is no excuse why someone cannot do nine minutes of exercise in a day, throughout the day. To make sure, we are adding a reward aspect to the app. We are creating the first crypto wellness token/coin. It will be called Fitcoin. For every exercise you do throughout your day, you will be compensated with a Fitcoin. What is the coin worth? What do you want more of—time off, money, or health? Each company can tailor their app to your liking.

"I believe in being physically and financially fit," Eric continued. "On the physical side, being active and fit is obviously important, and it keeps your mind in tune, also. The results have been impressive. I can say for someone who has no exercise in their current day, they will double their numbers/reps within the first two weeks. Look at these stats," he said, placing a sheet of paper before her.

	Week 1 Increase	Week 2 Increase	Total Increase
Desk Tricep Dips	43%	56%	133%
Desk Planks	0%	0%	0%
Squats	33%	14%	83%
High Knees	13%	24%	43%
Chair Sit ups	27%	-11%	50%
Side Leg Lifts	10%	9%	45%
Calf Raises	63%	10%	148%
Lunges	13%	9%	67%
Squats	29%	4%	60%

"Now, insofar as being financially fit, having the best credit score and financial background will provide people with opportunities and the ability to do what they want. I've found that most people don't know what's on their report," he said.

"I didn't, at least not until my divorce. That's when I had to give landlords permission to run my credit in order to get a lease," Sara said.

"You're not alone. Often, people wait until there's a need before they check their credit report. And it's also true that oftentimes they are surprised at what's in that report when they do see it," he shared. "The one thing I've learned is that people neglect their SOP."

"Standard operating procedure, right?" Sara verified.

"In this case, it's not that at all. It's seem on point," he explained.

"What does that mean?"

"I tell people to seem on point in whatever they do, whether it's personal or business. If someone wants something from you and you acknowledge the fact that they need something and let them know that you're on top of it, they develop a level of trust in you. If you seem on point about whatever people need and let them know you're on top of it, it makes others think that you really are someone they want to do business with or have a relationship with. When you seem on point, they trust the fact that they don't have to worry and that you're taking care of it, whatever it is that they need," Eric shared.

"I'm interested in hearing more."

"It's as basic as responding to someone. If you don't respond to an inquiry, people will look for other options. However, if you respond immediately and are on point, or you get in front of something before it actually happens, you'll meet or even exceed their expectations. This is especially true in first impressions. If you have a new customer or client, and they have doubts or questions, by seeming on point, you can stop issues from snowballing and getting much larger.

"For instance, I might point out potential credit issues to a client, before I know that it even exists. And I'll also tell them how I can help them if it proves to be an issue in their business or their personal finances. Then, if it does actually become an issue, they trust that I have a plan and will help them take care of it. It's about being proactive, which is important in the credit business and in your health."

"That's great advice. I've recently been investigating the prospect of buying a home for me and my daughter. I really need to check my credit again and see where I stand," Sara said.

"You didn't tell me you were looking to buy a house," Liz interjected.

"Well, it's my long-term plan, but I'm having difficulty finding a home that I feel I can afford that doesn't need major upgrades. There is a real lack of affordable housing for young people or single people like me who don't have substantial incomes. I might have to settle for a neighborhood I'm not fond of or, perhaps, an older home that will require a lot of work," Sara admitted.

"Good credit will give you an advantage," Eric said. "I'd be happy to help if you'd like."

"That would be awesome! I know it's time for me to put down some permanent roots, so I'll be giving you a call," Sara said.

"Perfect. Now, before the afternoon session begins, how about we do a one-minute exercise to get our hearts pumping a little?" he asked. "You'll see just how easy it is!"

Sara rose to the invitation quickly, then looked toward Liz, who was intently jotting notes down on the back of her notepad.

"Hey, Liz, aren't you going to join us?" she asked.

"Oh, yes," she looked up in surprise. "Sorry, I just need a minute to make a note of something first. It's something I need to stay on top of …"

"Stay on top of, get in front of … sounds like you aren't only seeming on point, but you are on point, Liz," Eric smiled. "I don't think you've ever forgotten to do anything. As a matter of fact, you do more in a day than anyone I know. Hurry up and finish so you can get your 60-second workout in, too."

"I've been doing One Minute Before for almost a year now. It's a great concept. Believe me, I'm an advocate. And I just thought of another concept that might be just as great, and I needed to give myself a reminder to start working on it as soon as I get back home," Liz replied, putting her pen down. "Okay, I'm ready, Eric. Let's show Sara here how it's done."

The Heroine's Journey:
Qi Secrets for Success

Featuring Nadia Linda Hole, MD

"There you are!" Liz exclaimed as she rounded the corner on the last day of the conference. "I've been looking for you."

"What's up, Liz?" Sara asked.

"Dr. Hole's scheduled to be on stage in a few minutes. She's a dear friend, and I so want you to hear her message. Believe me, it's an experience! Would you come join me?" Liz invited.

The two rushed to claim front row, center-stage seats just as Dr. Hole took the stage and introduced herself.

"Aloha! I'm Dr. Linda Nadia Hole MD. Who'd like more success? ... *and* what does 'success' mean to you?

"Let me start by sharing my success journey. Years ago, as a single mom of four, I ran a busy wholistic medical practice, with patients from around the world, from all walks of life, including Hollywood! They came for Qi-KHT needleless acupuncture for immediate pain and stress relief, as well as for QiGong 'miracle healing' for health and other challenges. They were often desperate to find relief for their pains—from relationships, addiction, cancer, paralysis, to mid-life crisis, etc. I got featured on local and national TV news and was worth more than seven figures.

"As much as I was 'successfully' serving, when I look back as a now grandmother, I realized that something was missing. I had forgotten to include me.

"I exhausted myself doing my best to make others happy, bent on the ol' build the castles and slay the dragon!' hero's journey to 'success.' So I'd like to share with you today a more inward, heart-centered, self-care, self-love, birthing your future self, heroine's journey that my own health collapse forced me to take. It's a journey, for both men and women, where we achieve more by doing less, focusing instead on simply loving, feeling, and being willing to receive. This allows the Great Qi to birth an even greater You, for greater success.

"FYI, the more aligned, grounded, clear, and free your Qi is, the more magically 'success' can happen. In the early days of Twitter, I'd watch the numbers of my followers increase or drop, following my Qi. During the pandemic, when I realigned my Qi, I received invites to three big gigs, out of the blue, overnight. What if, beyond all the marketing bells and whistles, your success depends more on your Qi, than anything else? May I share and demo for you some Qi secrets for this?"

Liz and Sarah, together with other members of the audience, eagerly nodded.

"1st Secret: Alignment - Stand Tall, *Ding Tian Li Di - Head touches sky, feet stand on earth.*

"Before starting your day, look at yourself in the mirror and check your alignment. Whatever you're feeling, whatever's happening, stand TALL, crown connected and open to the heavens, feet firmly planted and grounded on earth, for who you were born to truly be. Roll your shoulders back to let whatever burdens you're carrying roll off. Give yourself a deep breath, stand tall, and notice how you feel.

"Now check your *inner* alignment. To whom, or to what, are you giving 'leadership?' Old habitual voices, worries, concerns, and/or outer dramas that you've no control over?

"Give yourself a deep breath; listen deeply for the voice of your heart of hearts and the Great Qi. Do your best to give leadership, instead, to the still inner voice, and trust what the Qi reveals to you.

"2nd Secret: Clear Intention, *Yi Nian—Where attention goes, energy flows.*

"Whatever you focus on and fill your Qi field with is what you'll get. Who/what occupies your mental, emotional, and psychic real estate? Whoever and whatever no longer serves you, it's time to cut loose and let go of ASAP, period!!! Or else you'll keep replaying what no longer serves you.

"William Bengston, PhD, author of *The Energy Cure*, teaches a practice he calls *cycling*—rather than recycling the past, give yourself a deep breath and intentionally redirect your attention to cycling your heart-of-hearts happy bucket list: everything positive you want to create in your life. Do this for your future self, future life, and the better you that you're becoming.

"Dr. Bengston's cyclers consistently report miracles, in all aspects of their lives, from incurable cancer, to dream houses, projects, and more coming true.

"3rd Secret: Relax! *Fang Song—Let go* ... and Relax!

"Relax does not mean zoning out, slouching out, and/or distracting yourself with entertainment or substances. Fang Song more accurately means, 'Let Go and *Loosen* Yourself.'

"Give yourself three slow, deep belly breaths, as deep as you can, to expand your chest. Breathe in pure, clean, 'good' Qi. Breathe out *everything* else. Then *loosen* your grip on whatever you're holding on to. Intentionally *let go* and *release* whatever no longer serves you. Herbert Benson, MD, of *Harvard's Mind Body Institute*, writes in *The Relaxation Response* how this is one of the most powerful tools to neutralize fright or flight trauma reactions and help bring you back to a more balanced, pre-stress, state.

"4th Secret: Inner Smile of Gratitude and PMA Positive Mental Attitude, *Nei xin de wei xiao – Be in your heart and smile.*

"Dr. Martin Seligman, PhD, the founder of Positive Psychology, found in his research that the daily practice of identifying three things to be grateful for, for six months, has a significant impact on alleviating depression and increasing happiness.

"Shirzad Chamine, NYT best-selling author of *Positive Intelligence*, in his Fortune 500 work on having a more positive mental attitude, found in his 6-week program significant improvements in sales (37%), productivity (93%), and profits (34%).

"Other studies show that simply smiling has a positive measurable effect on your brain waves, HRV, nervous and immune systems, and more.

"So, no matter what, keep smiling!"

Smiling for emphasis, Dr. Nadia went on to share the fifth secret.

"5th secret: Good Fortune—*Hao Yun Qi* – 'Good Move Qi.'

"For good fortune, we must keep our Qi, our bodies, and our lives actively moving, in a positive direction. Qi that doesn't move becomes stagnant. To reach a destination, you must move.

"The more abundantly and freely your Qi flows, aligned with your highest good, the more good fortune and abundance can and will flow into your life.

"Find a simple set of Qi exercises to practice daily to keep your Qi flowing, *and* every day take some action in your life, one step at a time, toward your future self's bigger, greater life.

"6th Secret: Virtue and Values, *De.*

"Good business must be built on good values and virtue. What are your values? What's the virtue of your choices and actions?

"7th Secret: Connection & Relationships—*Lai Wang. Come and go, coming and going.*

"Good business is built on good relationships with authentic connection. Especially in the wake of these past two years, people more than ever need connection. The key relationship is, of course, your relationship with yourself and the Great Qi.

"8th Secret: The last and first secret is the Breath of Aloha—the miraculous breath of love, life, healing, and joy. Let's close with practicing this together. Put one hand on your heart charka and repeat 'Aloha' again and again, till you feel your heart chakra vibrating under your hand. Put your other hand on your belly. Breathe down into your belly. Allow the breath of Aloha to melt all stuck Qi and birth you!

"With every breath, practice remembering to breathe in only 'good' Qi. Deep breath in. Deep breath out. Breathe everything and everyone else out! Allow the Breath of Aloha free you to feel, let go, love, and be loved. As corny as this may sound, it's what the world, and each and every one of us, need the most now— love sweet love. In stillness, trust that the Great Qi has got you covered for a better, more Qi-filled world, a world of more Peace, Love, Justice, Mercy, Happiness, and Freedom for you and our children, too.

"Aloha, Aloha, Aloha… "

As Sara and the rest of the room chimed in, practicing the Aloha breath, she noticed a sense of calm come across the room. All of the background noise that had been constant throughout the afternoon was gone, replaced with peace and acceptance.

Sara found it extremely relaxing, and as Dr. Hole closed out the conference, she suddenly felt that everything was going to be okay. She needed to let go of her doubts and fears and focus on finding the joy in the process, regardless of what life brought her way. She had gone through trying times, but she had survived. Now, it was time for her to focus on the present and the future. She was in a place of new beginnings. The cords of the past needed to be cut, and it was time to start afresh and anew.

20

Become a Scrum Master

Featuring Felipe Engineer

On warm, sunny days, Sara often waited outside the train station, but on this particular morning, it was raining so she walked into the train station. As usual, there were plenty of empty seats in Station 42, but this time, she noticed there were a couple other passengers seeking shelter inside.

When the train approached, one of the passengers stepped aside to let her board before him, and he took a seat directly across the aisle from Sara.

"It was kind of you to let me board first, especially in this rain. Thank you," she said. Then following Liz's lead, she introduced herself and asked the man where he was going.

"I actually have an appointment at Roberts Development Company this morning," he said.

"Really? I work at Roberts! What a small world," Sara exclaimed. "Will you be meeting with Elizabeth Roberts?"

"Yes. I understand that others may join us, though. My name is Felipe Engineer. Ironically, Engineer is my last name, but I do have an electrical engineering degree and have worked in construction since college. I've been working for general contractors for more than 20 years. Actually, I've had the pleasure of working for three. In my current role, I'm focused on lean construction principles and techniques, which are borrowed and adopted from lean manufacturing companies like Toyota. Some of the pioneers in that area might be names you recognize, like Peter Drucker and William Edwards Deming."

"Of course, I've heard of them," Sara nodded.

"A lot of what I do is based on a system called Scrum, a framework for management developed by one of my current mentors, Dr. Jeff Southerland. I've been a Scrum practitioner in my work, and it's fueled absolutely everything I do, including my construction podcast. Today, I am passionately working to help other people in the construction industry stay in the industry and thrive in the work that they do. So even though I work nationally for my company, my influence is international with the work I do and the partnerships I have in promoting this type of work everywhere, like I'll be doing at Roberts today," Felipe explained.

"Wow, I'm impressed. Go on. I'm listening," Sara encouraged.

"As a builder and developer, I'm going to be helping Liz on a new project. My passion for Scrum has helped me personally and professionally, and I believe it will have a very positive impact on the project," Felipe said. "It's a lightweight system that makes daily improvement a habit, and it builds in increased capacity over time. People that use it immediately double and triple, then double again, the value they deliver to their clients and customers."

"How does it work?" Sara asked.

"It's very simple. The first thing Liz needs to have is a vision of why she is developing this land. She can think about the people who will benefit from living there, and those people can guide her in her vision. This will help her hook onto improving the process every day. The framework all starts with that purpose," he said.

"Now, I'm sure you've heard the old adages, like this is the way we've always done it, if it ain't broke, don't fix it, some people are paid to do, not to think, and we are not reinventing the wheel. All of those are just deflections from changing habits. Trying something new is new to most people," Felipe said.

"It sure is, and I'm no exception," agreed Sara.

"The very first thing to do once you're clear on the vision is to prioritize the most valuable things, then break the work down into the simplest steps. You have to be honest with what you're going to be able to do each day. Then you just rinse and repeat. That's it in a nutshell," he explained.

"How can I best help Liz implement this system in her project?" asked Sara.

"That's a good question. I suggest you make a list of all the things that need to be done in order to undertake this development. In the next step, prioritize the list based on constraints that you foresee. It could be financing, time constraints, or whatever considerations there might be. Then take a portion of that list and put it into a single week of work and work on those things only.

You can always go back into the list, which we call a backlog, and add to it. As you work with the team, you should stay focused on those things that are the highest priority for the next five days," said Felipe.

"Every single day, look at what you're working on and ask yourself if there are any constraints or blockers that are stopping you from achieving your planned work. If there are, make that your priority for the day and subordinate everything to that. That will create breakthroughs, and it will also create rapid learning. At the end of the week, you'll take a moment to pause and review what you have gotten done with the people involved."

"It makes sense," Sara nodded.

"It does. Of course, it's not just you. You'll have a team, I'm sure, and they should be involved. At the end of the week, the entire team should look at what went well and what could be better so you can identify one improvement you can make now. That improvement is the first thing you'll work on the next week. The cycle then gets repeated every single week. The outcome, Sara, is that your progress will go faster than anticipated. One of the keys that makes it so effective is that you're building in a habit of prioritizing and excitement in removing obstacles and constraints. In any project, change is guaranteed, so why not embrace those changes?"

"I can see how it would accelerate progress! And it sounds incredibly simple, which should bring the team on board!" Sara told him. "I'm sure I'll be part of the team, but I don't have oversight of the whole project. To be honest, I'm not very familiar with the details of the project."

"You might wonder why you just don't move ahead with the

project and do what other people tell you to do. To answer that, ask yourself four questions, Sara. First, what is your problem, struggle, or frustration with this unknown, new work you are going to undertake? Next, what is your current productivity level—how much are you getting done on a daily basis, and are you satisfied with it? Next, are you able to do what is needed to help deliver on your promises to the people who are depending on you? Then last, how will you know if you're improving?"

"Felipe, because this sounds so simple, how come I've never heard of it before?" Sara asked.

"For half of my career, I didn't know Scrum existed, either. I did what everyone else did and was told if I worked longer and harder than anyone else, I would achieve. That wasn't the case. Working more wasn't the solution. I was working too much and not being effective. Scrum changed my whole perspective in terms of what was valuable versus what wasn't valuable in terms of my customer. It helped me make decisions that allowed me to get more done and serve my client better. Now I work nationally spreading these tactics, values, and principles across the United States, and it has even taken me overseas and into South America multiple times," shared Felipe. "It transformed my way of working, and it improved my health because I now have time to treat myself better. It all stems from respect for yourself."

The engineer pulled the train into the station, coming to a full stop, and Sara and Felipe exited the car. As they walked into Liz's office, Sara couldn't wait to tell her that she just had to hear about Scrum.

"Felipe is the best Scrum Master. I've been an admirer of Scrum and his work for some time," Liz replied. "And I'm glad you had an opportunity to talk to him before we get started today, because *you* will be the one implementing Scrum in this project. Sara, this is your project from start to finish."

"It is? Me? I don't think I'm ready to take on a project on my own," Sara admitted.

"You are. I've made sure that you're ready. Besides, nobody else can oversee this project," Liz said.

"Why not?" asked Sara.

"Because it isn't mine to assign, Sara. It's yours. I've deeded the land to you. It's your dream to create new affordable homes for yourself and others like you. This is your opportunity to fulfill that dream and help others," Liz smiled. "And Felipe is here today to help you set up a system to make it happen."

Become an Abundant Wealth Creator

Featuring Angeline Wehmeyer

 Several months later, when Sara and Liz boarded the train to go home, Liz didn't sit next to her as usual. Instead, she smiled warmly at a woman who had previously boarded and sat next to her.

"Join us, Sara. I want you to meet my friend, Angeline Wehmeyer. Actually, she is my financial investor, but we've known each other long enough that we've become good friends. Angeline, allow me to introduce you to Sara Andrews, one of my assistants who I've also grown fond of," Liz said, introducing the two women.

"It's very good to meet you, Angeline," Sara smiled. "It's nice to see another friendly face on the train. Sometimes, it's just the two of us, right, Liz?"

"Yes, but once in a while, I'm fortunate to meet some fascinating people on the trip back and forth to Station 42," Liz remarked.

"Angeline is one of them."

"So, Angeline, you're an investor? That sounds like an interesting career," Sara said.

"Well, Sara, being an investor is only part of who I am. I am also an entrepreneur and a speaker," the woman said.

"I'm interested in learning more about investing, but it can be confusing. And I have no clue how to predict what will be a good investment, or a bad one, for that matter," Sara shared.

"I use something called a financial blueprint to identify the best investments for people. Then I help them put strategies and systems in place to give them financial protection and create a family legacy," advised Angeline.

"That sounds incredibly complicated," stated Sara.

"It doesn't have to be, although investments seem like a complex jungle, I help families find clarity and make the best choices for them and their family," Angeline said.

"What advice would you have for someone like me who is interested in venturing into investing in the next year or so. I'm nowhere near creating a legacy, to be honest, but would like to start small and go from there," Sara asked.

"Great question Sara, it really comes down to creating what YOU want. Most people are driven toward financial success by the expectations of others, maybe their parents, grandparents, or friends. This becomes a journey from a state of stress, anxiety, and fear. I encourage you to start from a place of inner abundance, a place of love and joy, and create a life that matters to you—not others," Angeline emphasized.

"Since we have a little time, let me share my story with you. Growing up in China, I was programmed by my parents to be a super achiever and work hard. When I was young, I was always driven and competitive. I went through life with the purpose of trying to get approval from my own mother. Later in life, when I was in college, I became a top student and even gave the commencement speech. That was a milestone for me and one of the proudest moments in my life. Naturally, I wanted my parents to be at my graduation, but they were too busy working and making a living to attend. That was very disappointing to me; it made me question myself, thinking that the only way I could get their approval was to work even harder and achieve even more."

"That's sad, and I can see how it would create a cycle of stress that would wear on anyone," Sara said.

"It did. Eventually, when I came to the U.S., I created amazing financial success, but I felt very empty. No matter what I did, there was a big hole deep inside that I could not fill. When I opened my first financial firm, I looked at my parents and knew deep inside they were proud, but they didn't show it on the outside," sighed Angeline.

"Finally, I realized the way I had been pursuing success was from a place of getting approval from my parents. My drive to success did not come from creating the life that I wanted. That realization created a shift in my mindset. I knew I wanted to live for me, not for someone else. At that moment, I made a decision and commitment that, for the rest of my life, I would take control and live life on my own terms, and create a life that fulfills me, not one that pleases my parents or society. Sara, wealth comes from a place of inner abundance, not outside approval."

"So can you share how I can start creating inner abundance?" asked Sara.

"Oh, yes, I would love to. The first thing you can do is discover yourself. Ask the big questions: Who am I? What is the meaning of my life? What is my purpose on this planet? What will I leave when I am gone? Those are the important things. At the end of the day, material things don't matter. You cannot take the money, the house, or the cars with you when you leave this world," Angeline shared.

"I agree," Sara nodded. "Both of my parents passed away last year, and I discovered quickly that the house and the material things are nice, but they weren't as important as my mom and dad believed they were."

"That's true. It's not about the physical things you leave behind — it's about the legacy you leave," advised Angeline. "As you go through the journey, discovering your true self, your meaning, and your purpose, you create more than wealth—you create a legacy. When you realize that, it makes a huge difference in your career and in your life. First, you will have a lot less stress, which is devastating in your health and relationships and, actually, in every aspect of your life. I still pursue my dreams and goals, but now I feel joyful and fulfilled during this process. I wake up excited—this is my life, and if I only have one chance to live, I want to make it count!"

"How do you make it count in a meaningful way, Angeline?"

"I ask myself two key questions: One, how impactful is my activity today? Two, how profound can I make this precious life that was given to me? When I answer those questions and live in alignment with the answers, I work less, have more fun, and make more money. It becomes a cycle of abundance, Sara, and that's how to build a lasting legacy. I want to impact people's lives, and I want to contribute to the success of others. In that way, we are leaving a legacy together. As I help you and others, it helps create both your legacy and mine."

"I am in the infancy of trying to build a legacy, Angeline. My husband and I divorced last year, and I always thought the legacy we'd leave our daughter would be *ours*—it would be a joint legacy. Now, I find I'm starting over and having to figure out how to leave her a legacy, and I don't know where to begin," admitted Sara.

"Start by accepting that whatever happened with your spouse, your kids, or your parents, happened. Take full responsibility for your life and realize that you cannot change it. Instead of blaming yourself and becoming a victim, recognize that you didn't know then what you know now. You cannot change the past, but from this moment forward, you can take responsibility for creating a life that truly matters to you, not to your ex-husband or anyone else. When you let go of the past, that's when your legacy can begin," Angeline smiled warmly.

"I encourage you to make sure that your life and your legacy are what *you* truly want. Be responsible for your own actions. Don't blame your past or a failed marriage. This is your opportunity to take control of your ship. *You* are the captain now! Be responsible for that! When you do that, you free yourself of the need for approval from anyone else," said Angeline.

"That's when financial wealth will enter my life?" asked Sara.

"No, that's when you are ready to receive wealth. You become an abundant wealth creator. Sara, you can't wait and hope for wealth to come to you. Create a mindset of abundance, and when you do, it is you that creates abundance *and* wealth in your life," Angeline said. "Actually, try to enjoy the process, this will be a fascinating time of discovery for you!"

"Speaking of time," Liz interjected. "Station 42 is around the bend. It was great to see you again, Angeline, but this is our stop. If you're free, let's meet for brunch soon."

"That sounds great! And, Sara, I'd also love you to join us, so I can hear about your journey," said Angeline.

"I'd love that, Angeline. And thank you for sharing your story and inspiring me to start taking responsibility for creating the legacy I want to leave. I've always been waiting for wealth to come to me, but it's no wonder that hasn't worked—I wasn't ready to receive wealth. Thanks to you, I'm going to change that, starting today."

22

The Secret's in the Sauce

Featuring Theresa Goss

As Sara focused on the plans for the residential subdivision, Liz was busily preparing for the town's biggest celebration—the town of Roberts was turning 150 years old, and its birthday was slated to be a grand-scale commemorative event. While Sara worked with surveyors and the town's planning department, Liz was chair of the committee that was planning the celebration. The festivities would open with a parade, followed by a festival that included carnival rides, food trucks, music by local bands, and sidewalk sales by retail stores and independent crafters.

It was in a regular weekly meeting that Liz informed her team of the plans to create a film documenting the town's history from its official founding to the present.

"That's wonderful, Liz," Sara said. "What a special way to honor your family and its contributions to the town!"

"Yes, it is. My grandfather would have been pleased, I'm sure. As it is, I am the only member of the Roberts family still in the area, so they are counting on me to provide them with important dates, photographs, and newspaper articles featuring our history. It's a task, believe me. Thankfully, my grandmother was quite the family historian, and she preserved important documents and articles. I just have to go through it all," Liz shared.

"How can we help?" Shannon asked.

"I'm glad you asked. I'll need someone to coordinate the details with the producer, and I also want someone to be available to assist the crew when the documentary is filmed. Any takers?"

Shannon immediately volunteered to serve as the coordinator, and Sara said she'd be happy to assist the crew with anything they needed. Several others chimed in, offering to lend a hand wherever they were needed. Liz had been good to all of them, and no one wanted to let her down.

"Thank you, everyone. Now, we better get busy. Filming starts next month, and we've got work to do!" Liz announced.

Excitement was in the air the day the filming began. Sara was there to meet the producer and her crew, and Liz had asked her to make sure she was available for anything they needed.

"It's very nice to meet you, Ms. Goss," Sara said, recognizing the producer from her online photograph.

"Ms. Goss? Oh, please, call me TGo—everyone does," was her enthused response.

"TGo it is! So, I don't know what's involved with producing a television show, so forgive me if I get in your way or don't know how to help," Sara said.

"Don't worry. You won't be in my way at all. I'm used to working around a lot of people and doing multiple things at once," TGo shared.

"I imagine that your career is demanding," Sara said. "How did you learn how to be a television producer. It seems like an unusual career path."

"Well, I am a television producer and the host of my own national television show, but I originally started in high school as a computer programmer. So you could say I'm a really creative person with a tech side. Considering my origins, you're right, it was an unlikely career path, to say the least," said TGo.

"Oh? What were those origins, if I can ask?"

"Starting at the beginning, I was born in Gary, Indiana, and I was adopted. My dad was a steel mill worker, and my mom was a seamstress at a sweatshop in Chicago. My parents were older, in their forties, when they adopted me. As sharecroppers, they didn't have a great education, and I was dyslexic, but gifted. However, my father didn't want me to go to school for the gifted, so I went to public school, where I was bored all the time. I didn't even go to my classes, but I always showed up for the tests.

"Then, my swim coach took me aside one day and told me she was afraid that she was going to lose me to gangs. She proceeded to take me into a room, where I was face to face with several giant computers. The teacher there told me he would teach me everything he knew about those computers, on one condition: I had to go to class."

"And what did you do?" asked Sara.

"Let's just say that I now program in 16 computer languages. I own streaming networks and produce television shows. We own studios, and by day, I have my own show, called Expert Talk with TGo. At night, I build the websites, create the apps, and do my super geek thing," she said.

"You're an over achiever! How do you find the time to do it all?"

"I don't know anything else. As a matter of fact, I'm always juggling various things at the same time. It's how I work," TGo shared.

"I don't know how you do it! My head would be spinning!" Sara admitted.

"My grandma used to say that the secret's in the sauce. It's what you have on the back stove that's cooking all the time. Right now today, that's media. If you want to duplicate yourself, it's not about working more hours. It's figuring out a way to get a message recorded or filmed and let it work for you while you're sleeping. Duplicate your message so it can function while you're sleeping or doing other things," TGo said.

"Really? I'm developing a tract of land and will eventually be selling more than 70 homes. How can I duplicate that message?" Sara asked.

"You can create advertisements or start a podcast so people can hear what you do and have to say anytime, anywhere. It doesn't matter if you're a developer or a salesperson. Anyone can duplicate themselves. They can do films, documentaries, television shows, or apps and duplicate the process to let it run while they're sleeping, dealing with kids, on vacation, or working on their next project," she explained. "Because if you're just working, you're never going to be able to make enough money to do multiple things or move on to the next stage. It's about duplicating your efforts so they're working for you, rather than constantly working and physically repeating those efforts over and over.

"Let me ask, Sara, are you going to spend 10 hours a day, every day, trying to sell these homes?" TGo asked.

"Oh, I hope not. I have a daughter at home and a job. There is no way I could find another 10 hours in my day," Sara sighed.

"Then you need to find a way to duplicate the process and reach more people than you would otherwise, so you can work and go home and spend time with your daughter—and make money at the same time!" TGo smiled.

"I'd love to be able to do that!"

"Sara, when people ask me what my definition of a good day is, I tell them it is when I wake up in the morning and my 15-year-old dog needs to go outside, and I look at my phone and see that I'd made $10,000 while I was sleeping. That's a good day. That's what I'm talking about!" TGo exclaimed.

"That would be absolutely amazing!"

"Believe me, once you figure out that the secret's in the sauce and that there's phenomenal power in duplicating yourself and your message, it's a game changer. You don't have to be a mega multitasker, like me. I think that's something that you have to be born with," she laughed. "But you can have systems and processes that are always working in the background, on the back burner, working for you while you're working ... or at the beach

… or on vacation, Sara."

"TGo, I think you might've just saved me hundreds of hours of work!" Sara exclaimed. "I know you said you were gifted, but I think you're a genius! I can't wait to get started, actually. Would it be okay if I reach out to you if I need some advice or assistance?"

"Would it be okay? It would be awesome! I'd love to help you; it's what I do! Meanwhile, it might help you to watch us today as we film. I think you'll learn a lot. That's how I learned so much of what I do. I worked side by side with other people, who taught me what to do and how to do it. From there, I used what I know to get to the next level or the next stage in my career," TGo said.

"Oh, I was hoping I'd have an opportunity to watch the show being filmed. Seeing it in the process from start to finish is like being in on a big secret," Sara replied.

"There's no secret to it, Sara. Remember where the secret is; it's in the sauce," the producer said before turning her attention toward the crews that were waiting for her instructions.

Discover the Art of Negotiation

Featuring Christine McKay

 For more than two months, Station 42 had been closed to the public, according to a sign that was posted on the entrance stating that it was "under construction." Adjacent to that sign was a notice providing a phone number and a website for anyone needing assistance. Passengers were invited to wait for their train in the temporary shelter that had been erected outside the station.

Sara found that she really missed spending her mornings inside the train station. The historic building had become familiar to her, and she had enjoyed the opportunity it gave her to talk to new people who were waiting to board their trains—people like Eric Power, who she had now seen several times since she'd started taking the train daily to her job at Roberts Development.

However, since the station had closed, she noticed that it was far more common for her to be the only person waiting in the temporary shelter. She guessed that people preferred to drive or hire a service to take them where they wanted to go, rather than wait outdoors. They weren't alone; it was a chilly and rainy morning when Sara dashed into the shelter, wishing she had chosen another mode of transportation, especially since her train wasn't scheduled to arrive for nearly 20 more minutes.

But on this morning, to her surprise, Sara was joined by another woman.

"Miserable out there, isn't it?" she asked.

"Oh, yes, it is. I almost turned around and went back home," the woman laughed. "I probably would have if I didn't have a meeting in town. Actually, I rarely take the train, but my car is in the shop right now. I wish I had known the station was closed, though."

"You said you have a meeting in town. It wouldn't happen to be the monthly small business owners meeting, would it? I know they're in the midst of preparing for Roberts' upcoming festivities," Sara said, remembering that it had been on her employer's calendar.

"Yes, as a matter of fact, it is. Are you attending?"

"Oh, no. But my employer, Elizabeth Roberts, will be there," Sara replied.

"You work for Liz? What a small world! I'm Christine McKay, and I've been a friend of the Roberts family for years."

"It's good to meet you, Christine! My name is Sara Andrews. So I take it that you are a member of the Small Business Association?"

"Actually, I will be attending today as their featured speaker, sharing my programs that help small companies ask for more of what they want and then showing them how to negotiate for it. But I will certainly stick around to hear what they have planned for the town-wide festival," Christine explained.

"Negotiating? That sounds fascinating," Sara responded. "Perhaps you can help me, when I get my small business on its feet, that is."

A few minutes later, Sara had given Christine an overview of that business.

"We are just beginning the process, to be honest. I have the land, but I'm in the beginning stages of actually creating the development. It'll house 74 premanufactured homes that are intended to appeal to young families. My goal is to make home ownership affordable for this demographic, something that has been lacking for some time. My goal is to also create what Liz calls 'passive income' by selling the homes but retaining ownership of the lots they are on. The buyers will then pay monthly rent for the lot and certain utilities. The development will take care of mowing the grass and raking the leaves. It's a new and exciting venture for me, and I have to admit that it scares me so much that it keeps me up at night sometimes," Sara stated.

"Why does it scare you?" asked Christine.

"I guess because I've never owned a business before. And then there's the fact that I'm a single mom and don't have anyone to fall back on," Sara said, clicking off her reasons.

"Well, Sara, if I could manage to find a way to become a success with everything that I had going against me, I assure you that you can, too," Christine said. "Like you, I was a single mom at a young age, and with no money or support, I found myself living in my car, a Chrysler Newport. Obviously, I needed help, but I didn't know how to help myself, so I married a man who I trusted to take care of me. Before I knew it, I was 22 years old and the mother of three daughters. However, my husband wasn't supporting us, and he didn't allow me to work. Food banks and churches provided whatever groceries we had, and we used a stove to heat our house and boil water for bathing."

"Oh, my, that sounds terrible. How did you rise above it?" Sara asked.

"I knew I couldn't live that way any longer, and I also knew that the way out of poverty was education, so I enrolled in our local community college. It was hard—I had to study between 3:00 and 6:00 a.m. because my husband didn't allow me to study when the children were awake. But I did it! I graduated with a 4.0 GPA and earned a scholarship to Rensselaer Polytechnic Institute. The minute I stepped on campus, I knew what I had to do and went home and asked my husband for a divorce," said Christine.

"Good for you! But it must've been hard to earn your degree on your own," Sara remarked.

"Being a single mom and a full-time student isn't easy, and I still had to swallow my pride and apply for welfare and assistance. I'll never forget the day that I told the woman at the welfare office that I was going to go to Harvard someday."

"Did you?"

"Go to Harvard? Yes, I did. I graduated cum laude from Rensselaer and that changed my life. I married a wonderful man and eventually got a job in international finance. That's when I realized that I needed to be an MBA in order to take my career to the next level, so I applied to Harvard and was accepted," Christine smiled. "Today, I use that MBA to advise companies of all sizes, from small businesses to Fortune 500s, and help them negotiate for what they want."

"That's an amazing story. Oh, I'd love to have a happy ending like that," Sara sighed. "But I don't even know how to go about making that happen."

"Just ask," Christine responded quickly. "I've learned that people are afraid to ask for help, but they shouldn't be. They're afraid to ask for opinions or advice because they think they're bothering someone. They're afraid they're not worthy of other people's time or expertise. And I've even seen people who are reluctant to ask for advice or support because they don't think they're worthy of it or they're too proud. Sara, I'm here to tell you that none of those reasons are valid. People do genuinely want to help others, but most people don't know that because they're too afraid to ask them in the first place," Christine explained. "There was a time when I didn't want to ask for help, either, but I know now that I wouldn't be a success today if I hadn't."

"You have a point," Sara smiled. "The next time I need something, I'll keep that in mind."

"Do it. Ask for what you want. Don't stop and think that you don't deserve it—you do. Don't wonder if you're asking for too much because then you'll end up asking for less. Ask, then you'll get your answer. If that answer isn't what you want, negotiate! Don't be intimidated because this is new to you—you have the right to negotiate your business and your life, Sara. It's the only way to make sure you aren't settling for less than you deserve," said Christine.

"I wish I had as much faith in myself as you do," Sara countered.

"Hey, there was a time when I didn't have any faith in myself. I didn't trust myself to make a single decision back when I was a homeless single mom. But I learned to surround myself with people who had the faith that I lacked, including my current husband, and because of them, I managed to overcome my own lack of confidence. You see, while I didn't have faith in myself, their faith in me never wavered, and they gave me the support and encouragement I needed to believe in myself. If you don't have faith in yourself, Sara, surround yourself with people who do have faith in you. It's the greatest gift you'll give yourself in life," Christine advised.

"I think I already have," Sara smiled. "Liz has been a blessing to me, and so has my daughter. I'm going to take your advice, Christine, because I can't let them down."

"I'm really glad to hear it," Christine replied. "And if you find you need anything, anything at all—a friendly ear, some professional guidance, or a crash course in negotiating—you know what you have to do."

"Just ask," Sara grinned as she tucked Christine's business card into her bag just as the train whistle blew, signifying that her train was approaching Station 42.

(24)

Celebrating Legacies New and Old

The renovations to Station 42 continued, and Sara grew accustomed to waiting in the temporary shelter to board her morning train. One morning, she contemplated how much her life had changed since that fateful day when she found the envelope that contained the open-ended ticket from her grandparents.

Never in her wildest imagination had she thought that Station 42, which she had never visited in her life a few years before, would become a mainstay of her work week.

And she had her grandparents to thank for it.

There was no way they could have known the impact that a long-lost letter to their granddaughter would have made on her life so many years later. Sara knew in her heart that without that letter and the ticket her grandparents gifted, she would have never met Liz or so many other people who had influenced her life at a time when she needed it most.

These people became her friends, mentors, coaches, consultants, and her tribe. Because of them, she had a newfound confidence and had found emotional happiness. She was now, by all definitions, a businesswoman who had a career and a future she could be proud of. Most of all, she had become a role model to her daughter and was proving to her by example that she, too, could accomplish anything she wanted, whether it was opening her own juice bar or earning a PhD.

Of course, it hadn't been easy, especially when she embarked on the development of the land that Liz had gifted her.

To Liz, it might have seemed like a small-scale project, but to Sara, it was everything and more. And she wanted every detail to be perfect, which she quickly learned wasn't possible. But with the right systems in place, she was able to overcome challenges and reverse course when needed. That was vital, especially when she had to work with so many different agencies, regulations, and people.

Sara had discovered that Liz had purchased the land more than a decade before, in a time when businesses were struggling, and the economy had put the brakes on new construction. Liz explained that Roberts Development bought the land below market price back then, and she'd held onto it ever since, knowing that one day an opportunity would present itself and the land would increase in value.

That day came when Liz was contacted by an online retail giant that was interested in purchasing a large section of acreage on which to build a new facility that would add 400-plus jobs to the community.

All it took was for word to get out to get the ball rolling.

With a large facility employing so many, there was suddenly interest in retail and commercial development in the area nearby. A gas station and convenience store were the first to put an offer in for a piece of adjacent land, followed by a couple fast food restaurants and a coffee shop. From there, it didn't take long before Liz was approached by a retail developer interested in opening a strip mall. Not only was this property on the outskirts of town suddenly a hot commodity, but the buyers were bringing with them more and more jobs.

That was when the idea came to Liz. Additional jobs and development in the community meant a need for additional housing ... and Sara's desire to create affordable housing was the perfect solution to meet the needs that would arise from the booming development.

She knew there was a market for housing for this demographic; however, commercial and industrial development had been the focus at Roberts Development. As she contemplated whether she wanted to expand their focus for this particular project, she realized that there was another option.

She had trained Sara for this, and she knew she was ready. She knew the ins and outs of rezoning property and had a great relationship with surveyors and the planning commission. To assist her, Liz had an impressive portfolio of contractors and architects who had the expertise to lend. Besides, Sara knew what was lacking in the real estate market, and her input and ideas would be invaluable. Liz was sure of that.

So when Liz contemplated what to do, she was sure she was doing the right thing when she deeded the land to Sara. But she wanted to do more than give her a gift—she wanted to give her the gift of financial security.

That's when she came up with the plan for Sara to not only build houses, but to lease the property. It was a win-win for everyone. Homeowners wouldn't have to purchase the land or worry about lawncare, and Sara could have a steady stream of passive income, providing her with additional cash flow and savings that she could hopefully reinvest in other projects down the road.

Sara and Abby had grown dear to her, and before Liz retired, this was just one of many things she wanted to do to make a difference, not only for them, but for the community that she loved.

Since then, Sara's life had been a whirlwind of activity, and she loved every minute of it, from the initial moments of doubt and trepidation right up to the celebratory groundbreaking, which was just one week away.

Telling Sara not to worry about anything, Liz and Shannon had made all of the plans.

The groundbreaking would occur the next Saturday, the same day that TGo's documentary about Liz and the town of Roberts was slated to debut at none other than Station 42. Sara had voiced concerns about the renovations taking place at the train station, but Liz assured her that Shannon had verified that everything would be completed prior to the event and the doors would be open to the public once again.

Sitting in the temporary shelter outside the train station, Sara wasn't so sure. Barricades still blocked the doors, and plastic sheeting covered the windows of the train depot, and there wasn't a soul in sight.

***

The weather cooperated fully on the day of the groundbreaking, which was one less thing for Sara to worry about as she stood next to the newly erected sign designating the subdivision as Bordertown Homes, a Roberts-Andrews Development. As she admired the sign, she was joined by Liz, several county and village officials, and her daughter, Abby, who was beaming with pride when Sara dedicated the development to her before ceremoniously breaking the ground with the very same shovel that Elizabeth Roberts's grandfather had used so many years before.

A few flashes of the camera and requests for statements by the press, and it was over. The preparations were done, and the first phase of construction was slated to begin the very next week.

Hand in hand, Sara, Liz, and Abby walked to the car that was waiting to take them to Station 42, where the documentary about Liz and her family would debut and the festivities for the town's celebration would commence.

When they arrived, Sara was taken aback as soon as she stepped out of the car. The outside of the structure, which had been covered in heavy sheets of plastic for the last couple months, now boasted a new Station 42 sign in bold black letters. The formerly cracked walkway had been replaced with new paved bricks, reminiscent of the days when the structure had been built.

But it was the inside that took Sara's breath away. Everything that was old looked new again. The marble had been cleaned and polished until it gleamed, and the light now shone brightly through the windows, highlighting their architecture and the grand clock that had been restored to its former glory. Gone were the random seats that awaited passengers, for they had been replaced with comfortable seating arrangements and tables that welcomed conversation. Large elaborate chandeliers hung from the massive ceilings, providing an elegance to the train station that would take anyone back in time.

It was all so new, so breathtaking! Everywhere Sara looked, she gasped … the rich dark wood that composed the ticket windows was newly stained and varnished, and Sara reminded herself that such intricate woodwork was a thing of the past. Then, the aroma of food led her to a newly built "Chef's Station" where a gentleman in an official chef's hat was filling platters of enticing appetizers for the guests. Turning around, the opposite wall now housed a coffee and pastry bar that would be perfect for early-morning passengers.

As Shannon led them on a brief tour, she opened a door that led to a private room that would be available to rent for parties and events. Nothing had been overlooked in the renovations, and the result was simply magnificent.

Station 42 had been restored to its former glamor and glory. It was once again fitting for grand occasions, just like it had been years ago when her parents and grandparents had frequented the train station, dressed in their finest and best.

As everyone exclaimed over the transformation, TGo approached them.

"Great job, Liz! This place is amazing!" she said.

"It turned out even better than I thought it would," Liz agreed.

"What do you mean—great job, *Liz*?" Sara asked, confused.

"It's nothing, really," Liz explained. "You see, Station 42 has been a part of my life since I was a young girl. Over the years, I grew accustomed to its gradual deterioration. I took it for granted and failed to notice how much it had changed. That is until I met you, Sara, and you mentioned how much you would have liked to have seen it in its former glory. When I saw this historic piece of architecture through your eyes, I was saddened that this historic landmark had been neglected. The more I thought about it, the more I knew it was such a vital piece of Roberts's history that I had to do something to restore its splendor."

"You paid for all of this?" Sara asked, shocked.

"Let's just say I donated to a worthwhile cause," Liz smiled.

"It's absolutely spectacular, Liz," Sara said, hugging her friend.

"Thank you. And TGo is here today to take us back to the days when Station 42 was a hub of activity and the main mode of transportation for the people of Roberts," Liz shared.

"What a day for Roberts! This town is so lucky to have an incredible woman like you!" Sara exclaimed.

"Thank you, but I feel lucky, too. After all, I have the greatest team, incredible friends, and an amazing network of people to turn to whenever I need them. And I have you, Sara, and Abby," Liz said, giving the young girl a hug. "I don't have children of my own, but it is people like you who have become the family I hold dear. I am forever grateful for the relationships I have been blessed with."

"And to think, we wouldn't have ever met if it hadn't been for the fact that my grandparents sent me a train ticket almost three decades ago. My life changed the day I first walked into Station

42."

"So did mine," Liz smiled warmly.

"I wish my grandparents could have known that their gift transformed my life," Sara thought out loud.

"Maybe not in the way they thought it would, but I think they knew there is something special about Station 42. Maybe, fate knew it, too, making sure you found the ticket they sent you when you needed it the most," Liz proposed.

Just then, the lights dimmed, and the sound system came alive as the large media screen lit up to the opening credits of the documentary honoring Liz and the Roberts family.

"All aboard," the conductor announced. "Welcome to Station 42. Join us as we take a ride back in time to when Franklin Roberts, the founder of Roberts, had a dream to plant his roots near a river that borders two states. We'll discover how his dream gave birth to jobs, businesses, and this train station. May Station 42 continue to connect Roberts and its residents to cities and towns across the country, just as it has connected people within Roberts to each other for more than 100 years. And now our journey begins…"

About Greg S. Reid

For over 25 years, Greg has inspired millions of people to take personal responsibility to step into the potential of their greatness, and, as such, his life of contribution has been recognized by government leaders, a foreign Princess, as well as luminaries in education, business, and industry.

Mr. Reid has been published in over 120 books, including 32 bestsellers in 45 languages. Titles, such as *Stickability: The Power of Perseverance; The Millionaire Mentor*, and *Three Feet from Gold: Turn Your Obstacles into Opportunities*, have inspired countless readers to understand that the most valuable lessons we learn are also the easiest ones to apply.

Greg is known best for being the Founder of Secret Knock, a Forbes and Inc. magazine top-rated event focused on partnership, networking, and business development. He is the producer of the Oscar-qualified film, *Wish Man,* based on the creator of the Make A Wish Foundation.

For his work in mentoring youth in his hometown of San Diego, Mr. Reid was honored by the White House, where a former President commended Greg for positively working with youth through a local mentorship program.

And if that is not enough, recently Greg was honored with the star on the infamous Las Vegas Walk of Stars.

To learn more, visit Gregreid.com

STATION 42

Featured Contributors
and Thought Leaders

(in order of appearance)

Chapter 3: Ask Gus

Shannon Parsons is an empathetic leader, speaker, facilitator, and trainer to executives, entrepreneurs and business organizations who are ready to level up their expertise. To learn more, visit www.ShannonParsons.com or contact Shannon via email at shannon@gregreid.com

Chapter 4: Invest in Great Relationships

Bill Walsh is America's small business expert. He is a venture capitalist, keynote speaker, business coach, and bestselling author. As the founder and CEO of Powerteam International, he serves clients worldwide in the areas of venture funding and small business success coaching. Visit his website at www.BillWalsh360.com

Chapter 5: Be the Change You Wish to See

Emily Mishler is the Founder and Managing Director of the Cultivated Group. She specializes in business development, creative and brand strategy, strategic planning, and fundraising. Emily has raised and distributed over $20M of private investment for private clients, for-profit entities, and

NGO's. Learn more about Emily and how she inspires others to be the change they wish to see at TheCultivatedGroup.co

Chapter 6: Discover Your Greatness

Kelly Cardenas is a *Forbes* contributor, author, podcaster, the founder/CEO of a national multi-million-dollar brand, and a cultural efficiency coach. Kelly's system zeros in on the heartbeat of any organization, its people! Please visit KellyCardenas.com

Chapter 7: It Takes Courage, a Tribe, and a Coach

Mary-Frances Buckland is a Master Certified Life and Health Coach and the founder of Solnar Wellness, focusing on healing with the power of Spirit, Unity, Determination, and Attitude. She is also a Certified Reiki Practitioner and a Mastermind Certified Leader. Find her on Facebook at www.facebook.com/maryfrances.buckland or send an email to m.buckland66@yahoo.com

Chapter 8: Fail Fast

Eric Power served in the United States Navy for 10 years. He is the Chief Executive Officer of Veterans Disability Help, LLC, which has helped thousands of disabled veterans receive their VA benefits. Eric is also a bestselling author and standing Board Chairman for Brighter Future Charity, which helps children gain social life skills. Visit his website at https://veterandisabilityhelp.com/lions-den

Chapter 9: Follow the Leader

Tina Malsom is a Premier Director at #DnaDrops at APL GO. She is a Master Socialpreneur who has mastered the art of making money socializing, and building relationships and teams through online and offline marketing strategies. To learn more about Tina, please visit her websites: www.dnaformyhealth.com and www.TinaMalsom.com

Chapter 10: The Vision Creates Provision

Dr. Wendy Labat created The Financial Cures System™, which teaches strategies for financial mastery. She is the CEO of M3 Enterprises LLC, a tax preparation company, and Dr. Wendy Labat LLC, an entrepreneur and business development agency. To connect with Dr. Wendy, visit www.thefinancialcures.com

Chapter 11: The All-in Principle

Albert Corey is an accountant, entrepreneur, and business strategist. He is the Senior Accounting Advisor of Corey and Associates Accounting Services in Hialeah, Florida, which specializes in tax services, business startups, and corporate compliance. To learn more, visit http://1040w2.com

Chapter 12: The Way You Play Games is the Way You Play Life

Billy Siordia is the Vice President of Secret Knock, acclaimed by Forbes and Yahoo Finance as one of the top three events for entrepreneurs and business leaders to attend in 2022. Billy is also a Mastermind Association Leader and a bestselling coauthor. Visit www.secretknock.co to learn more or send an email to Billy@gregreid.com

Chapter 13: To Achieve Abundance, Create Value

Paul Hutchinson is a serial entrepreneur with over 20 successful companies. His expertise includes business development, marketing, and finance. Paul is also the founder of The Child Liberation Foundation (CLF). Discover more at www.PaulHutchinsonOfficial.com

Chapter 14: You Can Do Hard Things

Cynthia Caughie is an entrepreneur and Homerun Pizza restaurant owner. She is also a realtor and the bestselling author of *YOU Can Do Hard Things*. She is a passionate business owner who is excited about sharing her success tips with the world. Visit her website, www.CynthiaCaughie.com

Chapter 15: Live Your Legacy While Building It

Jen Du Plessis is America's Lifestyle Business Master. Jen was listed in the Top 200 of nationally-ranked mortgage originators and funded over $1 billion in mortgage loans during her 37-year tenure. She is a bestselling author, top podcast host, and charismatic speaker. Visit her website: www.JenDuPlessis.com

Chapter 17: The More You Give, the More You Get

Mike Berkowitz is the Director of Pacific Stem Cells LLC. He has 25 years of strategic sales, operational, and corporate management experience in the healthcare industry with expertise in medical technologies and telemedicine. Mr. Berkowitz also founded TeleHealthCare. Visit his website: www.pacificstemcells.com or email michaelberko@yahoo.com

Chapter 18: Seem on Point

Eric Stuerken is the cofounder of Better Qualified, a company that specializes in consumer and business credit. Eric also created One Minute Before, an app for corporate health and wellness. The app tells you to do an exercise every hour on the hour for one minute. He is creating the first crypto wellness token/coin called Fitcoin. For more information, send an email to eric@betterqualified.com

Chapter 19: The Heroine's Journey: Qi Secrets for Success

Nadia Linda Hole, MD, is a graduate of Duke, Princeton, and Oneness Universities. She has served on multiple faculties and is a published author in books and medical journals. Dr. Hole holds certifications from East West Academy of Healing Arts, China Healthways Institute, Avalon Institute, Jaffe Institute, KHT Teacher's Training, Mastering Alchemy, Lightworkers, and Celebrating Life. To learn more, visit www.AlohaMD.com

Chapter 20: Become a Scrum Master

Felipe Engineer is a best-selling author, international keynote speaker, The EBFC Show podcast host, and proven construction change-maker from million to billion dollar-sized projects and companies worldwide implementing Lean and Agile practices. He is a Registered Scrum Trainer™ and Registered Scrum Master™. You can contact Felipe at www.thefelipe.bio.link and www.theebfcshow.com

Chapter 21: Become an Abundant Wealth Creator

Angeline Wehmeyer is an entrepreneur, real estate investor, speaker, and author. She educates clients on the power of investing, using easy-to-understand wealth principles through her course offerings and individual coaching. She is also the founder of Financial Genius Academy. Visit www.AngelineWehmeyer.com to learn more.

Chapter 22: The Secret's in the Sauce

Theresa Goss (TGo) is a producer, author, speaker, coach, and the host of Expert Talk with TGo. She was inducted into the Nevada Women's Hall of Fame for Entertainment and Media and received the Athena International TV and Producer Award. The publisher of the first all-digital interactive magazine for African Americans, she has over 1.8 million subscribers. To learn more about TGo, visit her website at www.Tgo.fm

Chapter 23: Discover the Art of Negotiation

Christine McKay is a Business Negotiation Strategist and the CEO of Venn Negotiation, which she launched to find common ground, level the playing field, and resolve complex issues for her clients. With over 25 years of international and domestic experience, Christine improves profitability and operational effectiveness through strategic contract integration. Discover more at www.vennnegotiation.com

Made in the USA
Middletown, DE
01 March 2022